Fun-Time Phonics!™

Learning to Read

Fun-Time Phonics™ Series
📖 Learning To Read 📖 Reading Is Fun

Written by

Robert Femiano

© 2015
THE CRITICAL THINKING CO.™
www.CriticalThinking.com
Phone: 800-458-4849 • Fax: 541-756-1758
1991 Sherman Ave., Suite 200 • North Bend • OR 97459
ISBN 978-1-60144-578-0

Table of Contents

Beginning To Read 272-314

Words I Can Read 313

Introduction

The most effective path to teaching beginning reading requires students to have a prerequisite understanding of how speech and print are interconnected — specifically, the mechanism by which any spoken word can be codified into writing, sound by sound. Developing this prereading knowledge takes two steps: raising student awareness that spoken words are composed of individual sounds strung together, and helping them see that these "smallest bits of speech" (phonemes) can be transcribed into print via the alphabet letters. Once a student is armed with these basic insights on how the code works, reading becomes demystified; it is now a logical, pattern-based activity and, as such, is easily grasped by most people.

The first step in the *Fun-Time Phonics™* program, therefore, is to ensure these prereading skills are developed. There are 100 thinking activities designed to teach the phonemic and alphabetic skills that underpin beginning reading. In addition to its stated objective, each lesson intentionally builds vocabulary as well. As the teacher reads aloud the word for each picture, the student will hear/see/say new words, providing multiple avenues to improving their "meaning-making" and access to their "mental dictionary."

The initial 14 lessons are designed to increase student understanding around the individual sounds within a word, with particular attention on the vowel sound, because this "middle sound" controls the definition of a word. Consider, for example, *cat* versus *cut* or *coat* to see the powerful role a vowel plays in changing word meaning. The ability to manipulate this medial sound, therefore, is the key to successful reading.

Following those opening activities, the bulk of the remaining lessons focus on introducing the alphabet, beginning with the five vowels, then followed by the consonants in order. For simplicity, only the five short vowels sounds are taught in these activities, as heard in the words: *bat*, *bet*, *bit*, *bot*, and *but*. Here students learn to co-articulate each consonant with the five vowels, putting them one step away from effortlessly "sounding out" whole words for both writing and reading. The final six activities seamlessly move the student into fluently reading over 150 three-letter words, with comprehension.

A note from many years of teaching: Learning to swap vowels within a word is not easy for many students and is downright difficult for a few. Nonetheless, it remains the single most important building block in learning to read and should be mastered up front. On the plus side, once done, the student will have leaped the tallest hurdle in learning how to read — the rest is easy, with practice.

Enjoy the activities with your students, and before you know it, they will be reading words, making meaning, and asking to start *Fun-Time Phonics™ Part 2: Reading Is Fun.*

Teaching Suggestions

Sequence and Mastery

Each lesson scaffolds on previous learning, so general mastery is important before moving on. The initial activities build the phonological awareness needed for a student to identify the individual phonemes within a word. These phonemic lessons end with a student being able to substitute one vowel sound for another, as in *hat* versus *hit* or *hot*. At that point the activities switch over to learning how to encode these sounds into print via the alphabet. This Alphabet Principle, as it is called, comprises the bulk of the lessons in this book as students learn both the letter names and sounds (co-articulated with a short vowel).

Vocabulary

An important part of reading skills is vocabulary development since making meaning of text is the goal. Allow ample time to discuss the pictures, in particular talking about unfamiliar ones, to help build an understanding for context in later reading. It may help to have the student re-explain those unfamiliar words after the lesson is completed—so you can determine their true understanding.

Multiple Meanings

Many words can mean more than one thing. For example, the word "tip" can mean the top of something, to fall, or to leave money for the server. But as a student once reminded me, it can also be what his grandad had at the race track! Try to be cognizant of the various uses for a word and share as the occasion arises.

Modeling

There are certain features or conventions of print unique to English that a child must be taught, such as reading from left to right and from top to bottom, or that capital and lowercase letters both make the same sound, while punctuation marks make no sound. By direct modeling and explicit instruction, teachers can make sure students begin to grasp these key components to the code we call print. When speaking, pay attention to enunciating all the sounds in a word, particularly the endings, which native speakers tend to drop.

Writing

The physical act of writing has been shown to improve memory. Depending on the student's age, printing the answer under the correct picture with a pencil or even "two-finger writing" of the letter(s) could be beneficial. It is also a chance to model the correct way to form letters; however, do not let it become frustrating, as reading is the goal here.

Motivation

Have fun with it. The joy of reading is transmitted through your interactions, so let them see you laugh and enjoy language while keeping the lessons lighthearted and positive. Celebrate completing a difficult activity by reading them a book or telling them a story!

Maintaining Focus

Young children can be easily distracted. To help them focus on the problem at hand, and avoid being distracted by other graphics on the page, try using blank sheets of paper to cover all but one row at a time on each page.

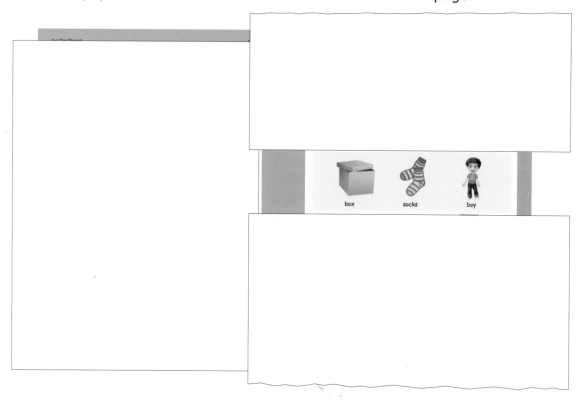

About the Author

After 37 years in the classroom, Presidential award-winning educator Robert Femiano now shares his highly-successful techniques for teaching beginning readers. In addition to his bachelor's in elementary education and his master's in child development, he was also adjunct faculty at Seattle Pacific University for more than a decade, teaching a Beginning Reading Methods course. This combination of academics and experience in the early grades has enabled Robert to translate the "science behind reading" into "how-to teach it" in a remarkably easy, fun and thinking-oriented program suitable for individual use or with an entire classroom. Previous publications include *Balance Benders*™ logic problems and *Balance Math & More*™ computational puzzles.

Activity 1: Beginning Sounds

The first sound you hear in a word is called the beginning sound. The beginning sound in the words time and tape is /t/*. Listen to the word for each picture as I say them to you.

Point to the picture whose name begins with the sound /t/.

top

pig

hen

bug

ten

car

wet

pet

toys

*When a letter is printed between two slash marks, such as /t/, we should say the <u>sound</u> of the letter to the student, not the name of the letter.
Throughout the activities in this book be sure to enunciate all sounds in a word clearly, including the endings. This explicit modeling speeds up learning.

Activity 1: Beginning Sounds

Point to the picture whose name begins with the sound /m/.

map

jam

hammer

clam

ram

man

Point to the picture whose name begins with the sound /l/.

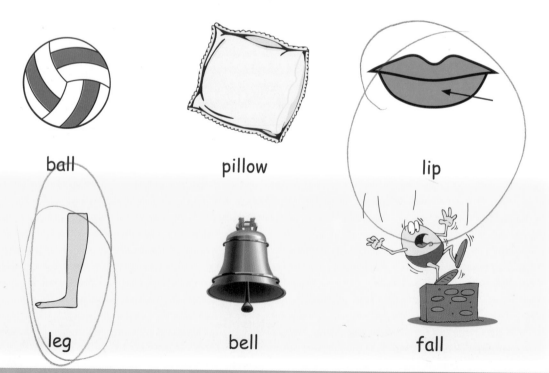

ball

pillow

lip

leg

bell

fall

Activity 1: Beginning Sounds

> Point to the picture whose name begins with the sound /n/.

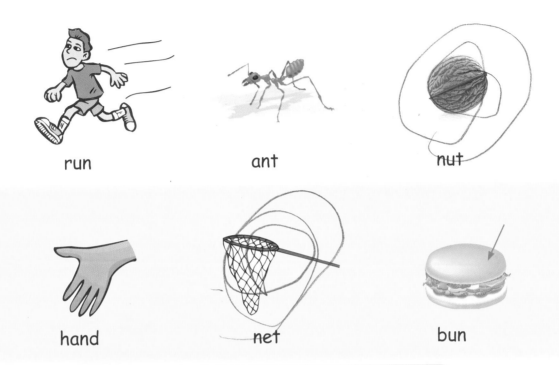

run

ant

nut

hand

net

bun

> Point to the picture whose name begins with the sound /r/.

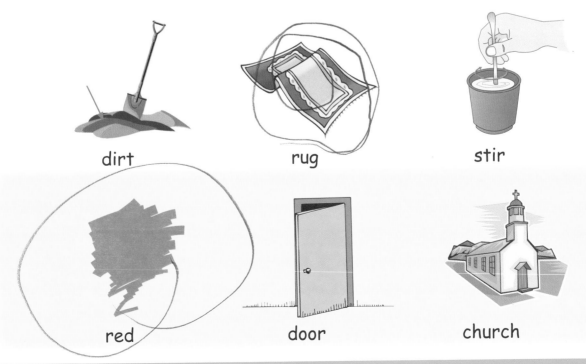

dirt

rug

stir

red

door

church

Activity 1: Beginning Sounds

Point to the picture whose name begins with the sound /g/.

gum   igloo   bug

hug   gym   girl

Point to the picture whose name begins with the sound /s/.

bus   zoo   sing

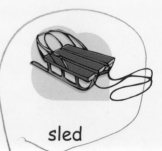

fish   ship   sled

Activity 2: Ending Sounds

The last sound you hear in a word is called the ending sound. The ending sound in the words hot and sit is /t/.

Point to the picture whose name ends with the sound /t/.

cat

fish

hop

butter

two

pot

stick

blast

sister

Activity 2: Ending Sounds

> ### Point to the picture whose name ends with the sound /d/.

dish

radio

mad

shade

dive

crab

> ### Point to the picture whose name ends with the sound /p/.

apple

pear

grape

crib

lips

slip

Activity 2: Ending Sounds

Point to the picture whose name
ends with the sound /k/.

truck

tickle

kite

kitchen

pickle

kick

Point to the picture whose name
ends with the sound /f/.

moth

laugh

~~office~~

coffee

bath

cliff

Activity 2: Ending Sounds

> Point to the picture whose name
> ends with the sound /m/.

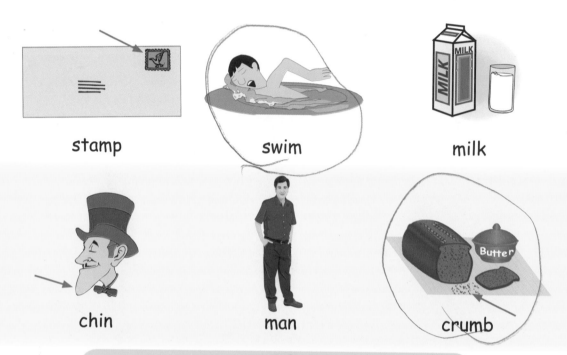

stamp   swim   milk

chin   man   crumb

> Point to the picture whose name
> ends with the sound /b/.

bud   grab   map

trap   globe   boxer

Activity 3:   Beginning and Ending Sounds

Point to the picture whose name begins with a different sound.

hop

dog

hot

box

socks

boy

ring

mad

monkey

chop

itch

chin

Activity 3: Beginning and Ending Sounds

> ### Point to the picture whose name begins with a different sound.

reading   bear   rose

trash   desk   dish

pot   pig   top

violin   fin   vase

Activity 3: Beginning and Ending Sounds

Point to the picture whose name begins with a different sound.

flag

frog

gopher

moth

thumb

thorn

swing

ice

stick

trick

drink

table

Activity 3:   Beginning and Ending Sounds

Point to the picture whose name
ends with a different sound.

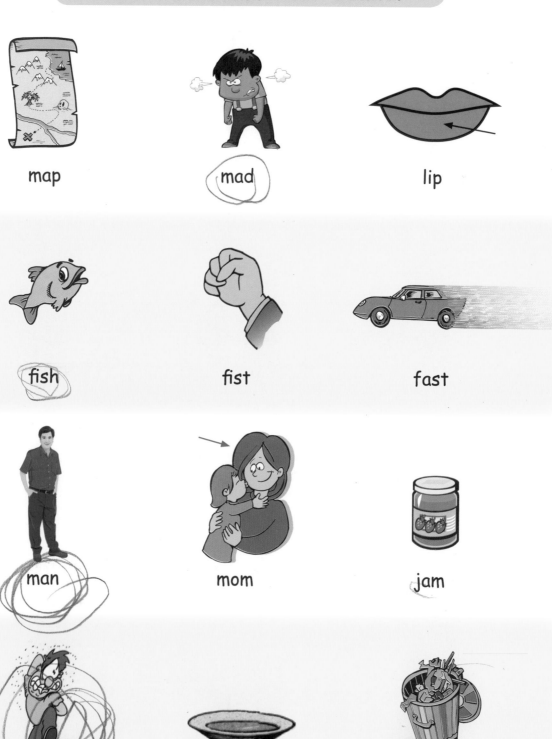

map

mad

lip

fish

fist

fast

man

mom

jam

itch

dish

trash

Activity 3:   Beginning and Ending Sounds

Point to the picture whose name ends with a different sound.

sleep   sheep   sheet

milk   spill   talk

hand   desk   yard

string   sink   sing

Activity 3: Beginning and Ending Sounds

Point to the picture whose name ends with a different sound.

blue   shoe   boot

snow   boat   piano

play   pail   spray

cowboy   oyster   fur

Activity 4: Rhyme Match

Words like red, head, and said rhyme because they all have the same ending sound of "ed." The words wait, late and great rhyme because they all end in "ate."

Point to the picture whose name rhymes with red.

hat   run   bed

Point to the picture whose name rhymes with fat.

mud   rat   sun

Point to the picture whose name rhymes with up.

bug   under   cup

Point to the picture whose name rhymes with ball.

pal   call   pill

A rhyme is that part of the word which contains the final vowel sound and ending consonants.

Activity 4: Rhyme Match

Point to the picture whose name rhymes with in.

chin

on

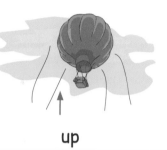

up

Point to the picture whose name rhymes with hop.

pup

drop

rug

Point to the picture whose name rhymes with wet.

deck

pet

wait

Point to the picture whose name rhymes with fish.

fists

kiss

dish

Activity 4: Rhyme Match

Point to the picture whose name rhymes with hot.

hut

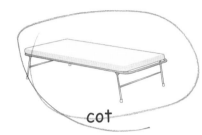

cot

hat

Point to the picture whose name rhymes with lip.

hip

crib

mop

Point to the picture whose name rhymes with egg.

bag

edge

beg

Point to the picture whose name rhymes with ax.

box

wax

black

Activity 4: Rhyme Match

Point to the picture whose name rhymes with **bath**.

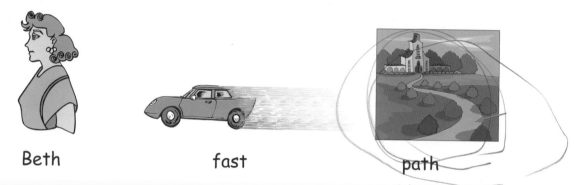

Beth   fast   path

Point to the picture whose name rhymes with **ox**.

hot   hogs   rocks

Point to the picture whose name rhymes with **head**.

hand   bread   heavy

Point to the picture whose name rhymes with **string**.

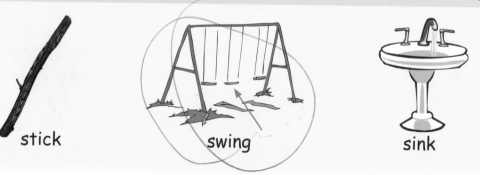

stick   swing   sink

Activity 4: Rhyme Match

Point to the picture whose name rhymes with ill.

drill

bell

doll

Point to the picture whose name rhymes with bench.

pitch

wrench

punch

Point to the picture whose name rhymes with truck.

bucket

duck

trunk

Point to the picture whose name rhymes with stamp.

stump

camp

plant

Activity 5: Rhyme Time

Listen to these four words: bug, rug, hug, sit. The word "sit" does not rhyme with the others. It does not end with the same /ug/ sound we hear in bug, rug, hug. Some words that rhyme with "sit" are bit, hit, and fit because they all end with the same /it/ sound.

Point to the two pictures that rhyme.

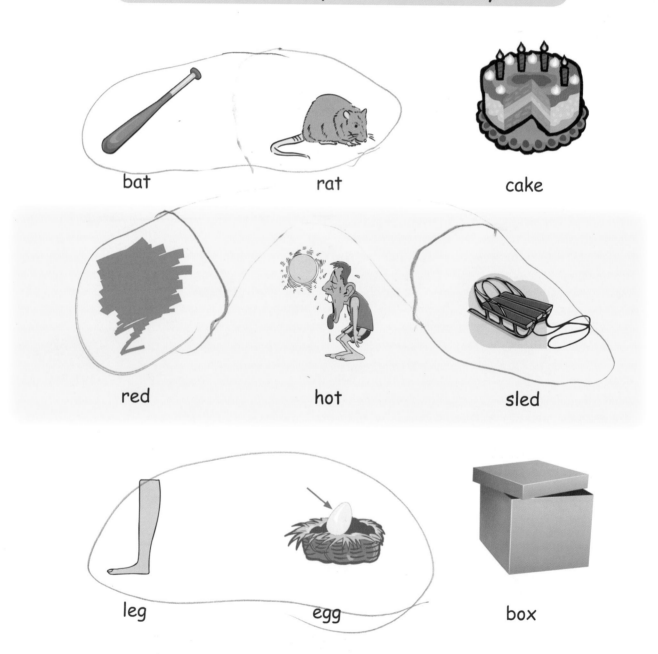

bat   rat   cake

red   hot   sled

leg   egg   box

Activity 5: Rhyme Time

Point to the two pictures that rhyme.

sit   hop   hit

mad   mask   bad

nine   run   sun

mop   cop   cup

Activity 5: Rhyme Time

Point to the two pictures that rhyme.

cap

ax

tacks

square

jar

bear

trip

trap

flip

shop

shot

cot

Activity 5: Rhyme Time

Point to the two pictures that rhyme.

stop

step

drop

ant

tent

plant

chin

shin

inch

thread

three

head

Activity 5: Rhyme Time

Point to the two pictures that rhyme.

sneeze   cheese   tree

in   on   pin

string   strong   king

shark   sharp   park

Activity 6: Say the Word

First I will say the name of each picture. Then I will say one of them very slowly. You say the word just as slowly, then point to the correct picture.

/eh/ /g/

box   egg   cat

/uh/ /p/

hot   cut   up

/ih/ /n/

in   on   under

The goal is to help the student understand that words are not a single sound but rather a string of sounds (phonemes) co-articulated as one sound.

Activity 6: Say the Word

/ah/ /cks/

ice

ax

ash

/oh/ /cks/

on

off

ox

/ah/ /d/

add

head

sad

/b/ /uh/ /g/

bug

dog

rug

Activity 6: Say the Word

/s/ /ih/ /t/

sick

sit

stick

/m/ /ah/ /d/

mad

mask

dad

/t/ /oh/ /p/

tape

tub

top

/r/ /eh/ /d/

road

red

wrench

Activity 6: Say the Word

/w/ /ih/ /g/

wag   wig   wick

/d/ /uh/ /k/

duck   dock   deck

/sh/ /oh/ /p/

chop   ship   shop

/ih/ /n/ /ch/

itch   inch   bench

Activity 7: Echo the Word

First I will say the name of each picture. Then I will say one of them very slowly. You say the word just as slowly, then point to the correct picture.

/k/ /ah/ /t/

cop

cut

cat

/m/ /oh/ /m/

mom

map

mop

/f/ /ih/ /l/

fall

ill

fill

The goal is to begin recognizing the vowel <u>sound</u> as separate from the beginning and ending consonant sounds. For many students, this difficult step is eased by the teacher elongating the vowel sound and increasing the volume slightly to focus their attention on this middle sound. This technique of stretching the vowel may prove helpful in the next five activities.

Activity 7: Echo the Word

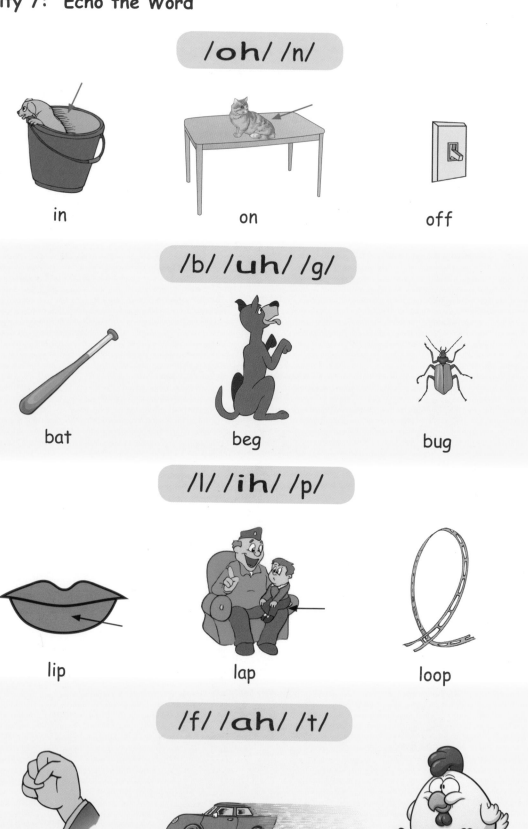

/oh/ /n/

in   on   off

/b/ /uh/ /g/

bat   beg   bug

/l/ /ih/ /p/

lip   lap   loop

/f/ /ah/ /t/

fist   fast   fat

Activity 7: Echo the Word

/m/ /eh/ /n/

moon

men

man

/r/ /eh/ /d/

road

bread

red

/sh/ /ih/ /n/

shin

ship

chin

/n/ /uh/ /t/

knot

nut

knight

Activity 7: Echo the Word

/s/ /ih/ /t/

cent

sit

sip

/r/ /uh/ /g/

rug

rag

wreck

/f/ /ih/ /s/ /t/

fish

fast

fist

/ch/ /oh/ /p/

chop

chip

shop

Activity 7: Echo the Word

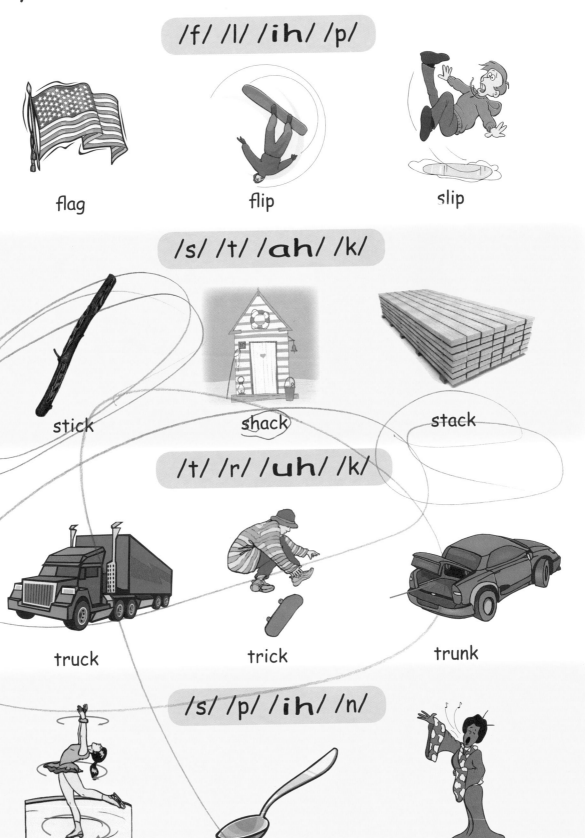

/f/ /l/ /ih/ /p/

flag

flip

slip

/s/ /t/ /ah/ /k/

stick

shack

stack

/t/ /r/ /uh/ /k/

truck

trick

trunk

/s/ /p/ /ih/ /n/

spin

spoon

sing

Activity 8: Find the Sound – Short a

> Point to the picture whose name has the /ah/ sound.

egg

apple

add

ape

pig

fix

ox

ax

It often helps students improve their accuracy to hear how their incorrect answer would sound if it did follow the directions. In the example above, if the student chose "egg" as having the /ah/ sound, the teacher could say, "We would have to call it an "ag" if it had the /ah/ sound." Giving students this important feedback (and giggling with them over the sometimes silly words) is a powerful technique useful throughout these beginning reading activities; it allows students to self-correct while maintaining a supportive environment.

Activity 8: Find the Sound – Short a

Point to the picture whose name has the /ah/ sound.

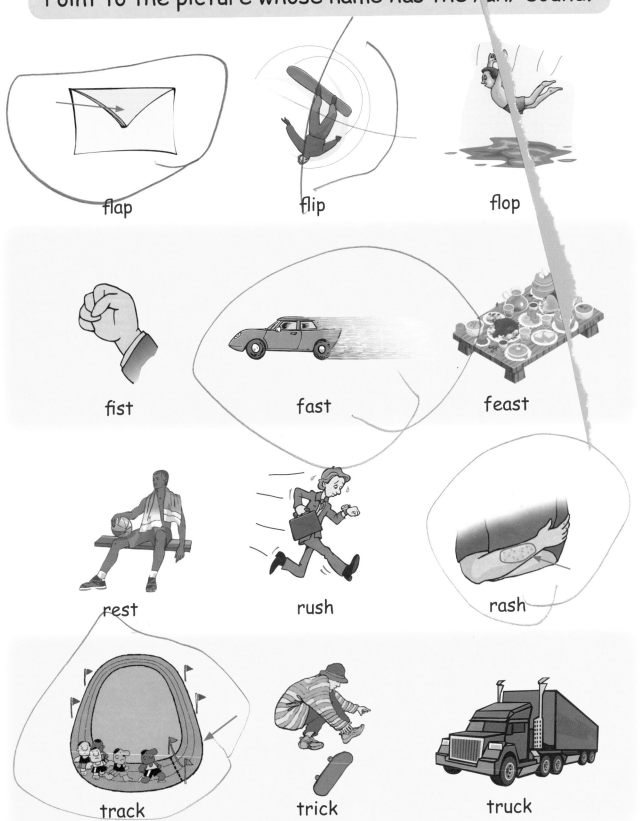

flap

flip

flop

fist

fast

feast

rest

rush

rash

track

trick

truck

Activity 8: Find the Sound – Short a

Point to the picture whose name has the /ah/ sound.

badge

bridge

edge

enter

wreck

actor

string

stretch

strap

screen

scratch

screw

Activity 9: Find the Sound – Short e

Point to the picture whose name has the /eh/ sound.

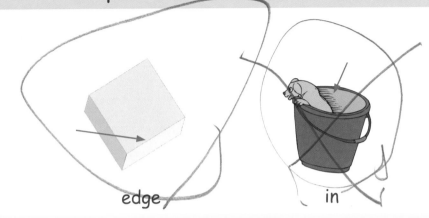

edge

in

on

end

under

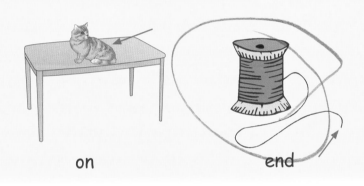

add

Ed

otter

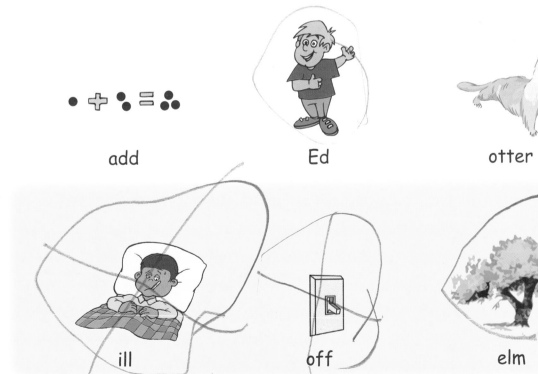

ill

off

elm

Activity 9: Find the Sound – Short e

> ## Point to the picture whose name has the /eh/ sound.

pet

pot

putt

white

wait

wet

pin

pen

pan

egg

igloo

ugly

The word "egg" is considered a short "e" word, but depending on dialect, it may sound more like a long "a." The same is true with the words leg, beg and peg.

Activity 9:   Find the Sound – Short e

Point to the picture whose name has the /eh/ sound.

sit   set   seat

bug   bag   beg

bed   bud   bid

MINTS

10

tin   ten   tan

Activity 9: Find the Sound – Short e

Point to the picture whose name has the /eh/ sound.

men

man

mom

dust

desk

dish

drip

drop

dress

pepper

bridge

cage

Activity 9: Find the Sound – Short e

Point to the picture whose name has the /eh/ sound.

chimp

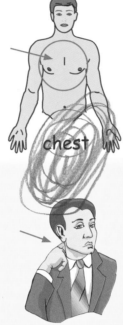

chest

chase

stitch

scratch

stretch

guests

gifts

glasses

father

fifteen

feather

Activity 10: Find the Sound – Short i

Point to the picture whose name has the /ih/ sound.

in

on

bell

ill

tall

rug

rag

rig

bug

beg

big

Activity 10: Find the Sound – Short i

Point to the picture whose name has the /ih/ sound.

pin

pen

pan

lap

lip

loop

boot

beet

bit

flip

flap

flop

Activity 10: Find the Sound – Short i

Point to the picture whose name has the /ih/ sound.

spine

spoon

spin

peg

pig

pug

punch

pitch

bench

Bob

Bill

Ben

Activity 10: Find the Sound – Short i

Point to the picture whose name has the /ih/ sound.

bed

bad

bid

slide

sled

slip

pit

pet

putt

watch

itch

wrench

Activity 10: Find the Sound – Short i

Point to the picture whose name has the /ih/ sound.

chess   chips   cheese

ships   shapes   shops

eagle   igloo   ugly

injured   enter   under

Activity 11: Find the Sound - Short o

Point to the picture whose name has the /oh/ sound.

ox

ax

in

on

out

hop

up

hip

ash

elk

otter

Activity 11: Find the Sound - Short o

Point to the picture whose name has the /oh/ sound.

hat

hut

hot

lock

lick

lake

pop

pipe

pup

pit

pet

pot

Activity 11: Find the Sound - Short o

Point to the picture whose name has the /oh/ sound.

Bob

bib

baby

fast

fix

fox

cup

cop

cap

drop

drip

droop

Activity 11: Find the Sound - Short o

Point to the picture whose name has the /oh/ sound.

shut   shot   sheet

flip   flap   flop

stop   step   stool

stomp   stamp   stump

Activity 12: Find the Sound – Short u

Point to the picture whose name has the /uh/ sound.

trick

truck

track

lunch

launch

latch

batter

boater

butter

wrist

rush

wrench

Activity 12: Find the sound – short u

Point to the picture whose name has the /uh/ sound.

stomp

stamp

stump

mud

mad

mitt

bench

punch

pitch

duck

dock

deck

Activity 13: Odd One Out

Which picture name has a different middle sound?

cat   cut   cap

sit   wig   bus

run   hen   bed

bug   sun   box

Activity 13:   Odd One Out

Which picture name has a different middle sound?

mad   mop   map

wet   hit   hill

pet   zip   desk

mud   hot   rug

Activity 13: Odd One Out

Which picture name has a different middle sound?

sit   set   red

pin   pen   lip

fox   bud   fun

clock   truck   drop

Activity 13: Odd One Out

Which picture name has a different middle sound?

| ship | dish | chef |

| feather | bread | father |

| stick | truck | trick |

| strap | stop | knot |

Activity 13: Odd One Out

Which picture name has a different middle sound?

brush

bridge

puddle

treasure

head

ladder

crumb

crab

tongue

sled

pitch

bench

Activity 14:   A New Word

If I take out the /ah/ sound from "bad" and put in the /eh/ sound, my new word is "bed." If I take out the /ih/ sound from "hit" and put in the /oh/ sound, my new word is "hot." Now you try it.

Take out the /ah/ from "cat" and put in /uh/. The new word is:

Take out the /ih/ from "bid" and put in /ah/. The new word is:

Take out the /oh/ from "hot" and put in /ih/. The new word is:

---

cot, cut, coat   bed, bud, bad   hit, hat, hut

Activity 14: A New Word

Take out the /ah/ from "cap" and put in /oh/. The new word is:

Take out the /eh/ from "bed" and put in /uh/. The new word is:

Take out the /ah/ from "tap" and put in /ih/. The new word is:

Take out the /uh/ from "bug" and put in /eh/. The new word is:

cape, cup, cop   bud, bird, bus   top, tip, tape   big, bag, beg

Activity 14: A New Word

Take out the /ih/ from "ship" and put in /oh/. The new word is:

Take out the /ah/ from "sat" and put in /eh/. The new word is:

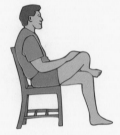  

Take out the /uh/ from "nut" and put in /eh/. The new word is:

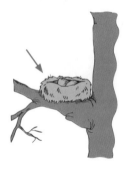  

Take out the /uh/ from "putt" and put in /ih/. The new word is:

chop, shop, shot   sit, set, seat   nest, net, knot   pot, pitch, pit

Activity 14: A New Word

Take out the /oh/ from "flop" and put in /ih/. The new word is:

 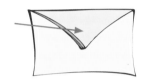 

Take out the /ah/ from "track" and put in /uh/. The new word is:

Take out the /ih/ from "fist" and put in /ah/. The new word is:

Take out the /eh/ from "better" and put in /uh/. The new word is:

lip, flap, flip   truck, trick, trunk   fish, fast, fat   batter, boater, butter

Learning to Read: Short Vowel Letters

 The letter "a" looks like this:

a   A

The letter "a" stands for the /ah/ sound in ax, apple, sad, and cat. We use the letter "a" to write words that have the /ah/ sound in them. When we read, the letter "a" tells us to say /ah/.

axe

apple

sad

cat

Explain that capital and lowercase letters may look different but they both stand for the same sound when writing or reading; we use capitals as a signal to the eye that the word is the name of someone or some place or the start of a sentence.

Activity 15: Connecting "a" With /ah/

Listen as I say each picture name. If you hear the /ah/ sound, that word is written with an "a."

Which picture name is written with an "a" in it?

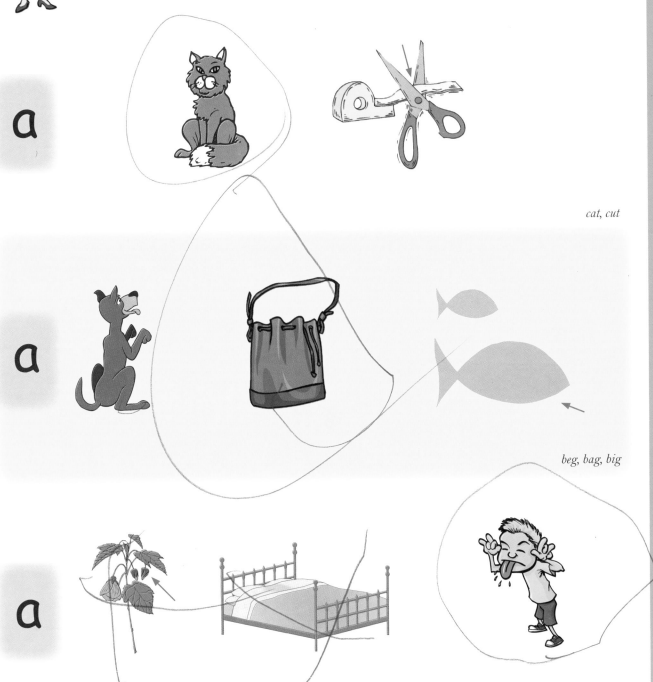

a

cat, cut

a

beg, bag, big

a

bud, bed, bad

Activity 15: Connecting "a" With /ah/

> # Which picture name is written with an "a" in it?

a

mud, mad, mitt

a

hit, hot, hat

a

cap, cop, cup

a

bit, beet, bat

Activity 15: Connecting "a" With /ah/

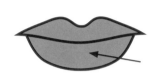

Which picture name is written with an "a" in it?

a

lap, lip, loop

a

sip, sap, soup

a

dig, drag, dog

a

mop, map, men

Activity 15: Connecting "a" With /ah/

Which picture name is written with an "a" in it?

a

flap, flip, flop

a

fist, fast, foot

a

rest, rush, rash

a

track, trick, truck

Activity 15:   Connecting "a" With /ah/

Which picture name is written with an "a" in it?

a

badge, bridge, edge

a

enter, under, actor

a

string, stretch, strap

a

screen, scratch, screw

Learning to Read: Short Vowel letters

 The letter "e" looks like this:

e   E

The letter "e" stands for the /eh/ sound in end, Ed, jet, and bed. We use the letter "e" to write words with the /eh/ sound in them. When we read, the letter "e" tells us to say /eh/.

end

Ed

jet

bed

Activity 16: Connecting "e" With /eh/

Listen as I say each picture name. If you hear the /eh/ sound, that word is written with an "e."

Which picture name is written with an "e" in it?

e

red, road

e

ball, bell, bull

e

knit, knot, net

Activity 16: Connecting "e" With /eh/

Which picture name is written with an "e" in it?

e

pet, pot, putt

e

white, wait, wet

e

pin, pen, pan

e

egg, igloo, ugly

Activity 16: Connecting "e" With /eh/

Which picture name is written with an "e" in it?

e

duck, dock, deck

e

bug, beg, bag

e

bud, bed, bid

e

ten, tin, tan

Activity 16: Connecting "e" With /eh/

Which picture name is written with an "e" in it?

e

men, man, mom

e

drip, drop, dress

e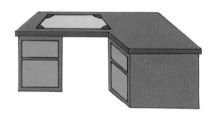

dust, desk, dish

e

bench, punch, pitch

Activity 16: Connecting "e" With /eh/

Which picture name is written with an "e" in it?

e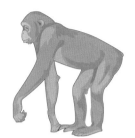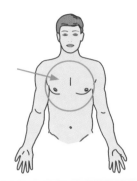

chimp, chest, chase

e

stitch, scratch, stretch

e

guests, gifts, gas

e

stop, step, stool

Learning to Read: Short Vowel Letters

 The letter "i" looks like this:

i I

The letter "i" stands for the /ih/ sound in itch, ill, kid, and sit. We use the letter "i" to write words that have the /ih/ sound in them. When we read, the letter "i" tells us to say /ih/.

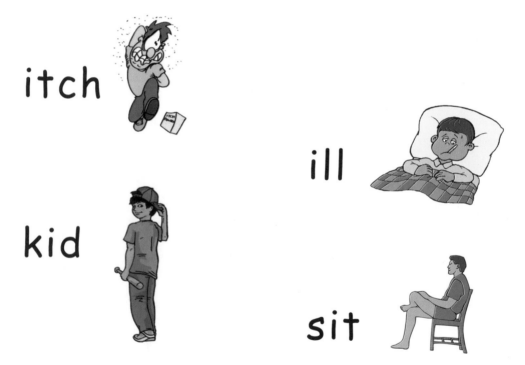

itch

ill

kid

sit

Activity 17: Connecting "i" With /ih/

Listen as I say each picture name. If you hear the /ih/ sound, that word is written with an "i."

Which picture name is written with an "i" in it?

i

in, on

i

bug, beg, big

i

fin, fan, fun

Activity 17: Connecting "i" With /ih/

Which picture name is written with an "i" in it?

pin, pen, pan

lap, lip, loop

sip, sap, soup

boot, beet, bit

Activity 17: Connecting "i" With /ih/

Which picture name is written with an "i" in it?

spin, spoon, sponge

peg, pig, pug

punch, pitch, bench

Ben, Bob, Bill

Activity 17: Connecting "i" With /ih/

Which picture name is written with an "i" in it?

bed, bad, bid

sleep, sled, slip

pit, pet, putt

pal, pill, pool

Activity 17: Connecting "i" With /ih/

> Which picture name is written with an "i" in it?

   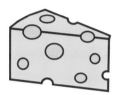

chess, chips, cheese

ships, shapes, shops

eagle, igloo, ugly

injured, enter, under

Learning to Read: Short Vowel Letters

The letter "o" looks like this:

o   O

The letter "o" stands for the /oh/ sound in otter, on, cop, and hot. We use the letter "o" to write words with the /oh/ sound in them. When we read, the letter "o" tells us to say /oh/.

otter

on

cop

hot

Activity 18: Connecting "o" With /oh/

Listen as I say each picture name. If you hear the /oh/ sound, that word is written with an "o."

Which picture name is written with an "o" in it?

O

hop, hip

O

elk, ox, ax

O

rock, rack, wreck

Activity 18: Connecting "o" With /oh/

Which picture name is written with an "o" in it?

 o

duck, dock, deck

o

lock, lick, lake

o

pop, pipe, pup

o

pit, pet, pot

Activity 18:   Connecting "o" With /oh/

Which picture name is written with an "o" in it?

Bob, bib, baby

fix, fast, fox

nut, gnat, knot

drip, drop, dress

Activity 18: Connecting "o" With /oh/

Which picture name is written with an "o" in it?

shut, shot, sheet

flip, flap, flop

stop, step, strap

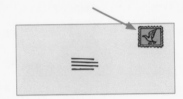

stomp, stamp, stump

Activity 18: Connecting "o" With /oh/

Which picture name is written with an "o" in it?

O

top, tip, tape

O

ships, shapes, shops

O

cot, cut, cat

O

sax, socks, six

Learning to Read: Short Vowel Letters

 This is the letter "u":

u   U

The letter "u" stands for the /uh/ sound in up, under, tub, and mud. We use the letter "u" to write words that have the /uh/ sound in them. When we read, the letter "u" tells us to say /uh/.

up

under

tub

mud

Activity 19: Connecting "u" With /uh/

Listen as I say each picture name. If you hear the /uh/ sound, that word is written with a "u."

Which picture name is written with a "u" in it?

u   

cup, cop

u         

eagle, igloo, ugly

u         

bone, bun, bin

Activity 19: Connecting "u" With /uh/

Which picture name is written with a "u" in it?

u

bug, bag, beg

u

kite, cat, cut

u

run, ring, rain

u

pop, pipe, pup

Activity 19: Connecting "u" With /uh/

Which picture name is written with a "u" in it?

u

fin, fan, fun

u

hat, hut, hot

u

boys, bees, bus

u

nut, net, knot

Activity 19:   Connecting "u" With /uh/

Which picture name is written with a "u" in it?

u

track, trick, truck

u

duck, dock, deck

u

rug, rag, rig

u

rest, rush, wrench

Activity 19: Connecting "u" With /uh/

> ### Which picture name is written with a "u" in it?

u
 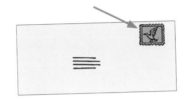 

stomp, stamp, stump

u

batter, boater, butter

u

bench, punch, pitch

u

puddle, paddle, poodle

Review: Connecting Short Vowel Sounds With Letters

Listen as I say each word. Repeat the middle sound aloud and then point to the letter used to write that sound.

Point to the letter used to write the middle sound in each word.

a   o   u

e   a   i

o   u   a

bug,   mad,   cop

Review: Connecting Short Vowel Sounds With Letters

Point to the letter used to write
the middle sound in each word.

a   e   u

i   o   a

e   a   i

u   o   a

red, pin, bat, box

Review: Connecting Short Vowel Sounds With Letters

Point to the letter used to write
the middle sound in each word.

e   o   u

e   i   o

i   u   a

u   a   o

sun, jet, fish, hop

Review: Connecting Short Vowel Sounds With Letters

Point to the letter used to write
the middle sound in each word.

10

i   a   e

o   u   i

e   a   o

u   o   a

ten, pill, lap, hug

Review: Connecting Short Vowel Sounds With Letters

When we read, the letters we see tell our brains to say their sound. When I see the letter "a," I say /ah/. When I see the letter "e," I say /eh/. When I see the letter "i," I think /ih/. The letter "o" makes me say /oh/, while the letter "u" makes me say /uh/.

Say the letter sound. Point to the picture whose name has that sound.

a

cat, cut, coat

e

bud, bed, bad

i

tip, tap, top

Review: Connecting Short Vowel Sounds With Letters

Say the letter sound. Point to the picture whose name has that sound.

o

sack, sock, sick

u

fin, fan, fun

e

bell, ball, bull

o

hat, hut, hot

Review: Connecting Short Vowel Sounds With Letters

Say the letter sound. Point to the
picture whose name has that sound.

u

  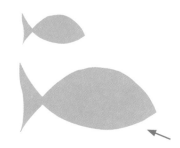

bug, bag, big

i

lap, lip, leap

a

baby, bed, bad

e

pin, pen, pan

Review: Connecting Short Vowel Sounds With Letters

Say the letter sound. Point to the
picture whose name has that sound.

o

lock, lick, lake

u

cap, cup, cape

i

knit, knot, net

e

bug, beg, big

Learning to Read: Consonants and Co-Articulation

This is the letter "b." The letter "b" looks like this:

b   B

"B" makes the beginning sound of bat, bed, big, box, and bug.

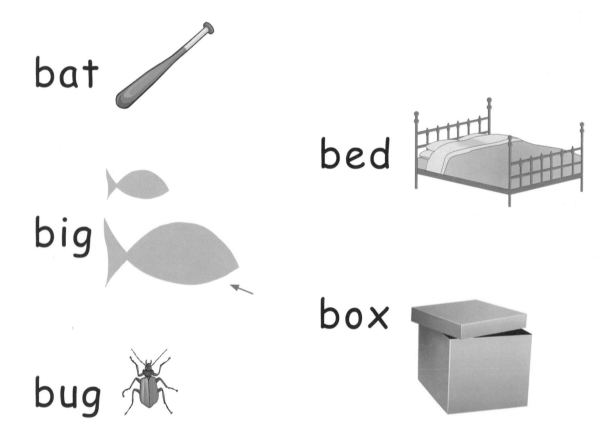

bat

bed

big

box

bug

Remind students that capital and lowercase letters may look different but they both make the same sound when reading; capital letters tell our brain that the word is the name of someone or some place or the start of a sentence.

Activity 20: Consonant With Short Vowel Sound - ba

Words like back, bath, and baboon all begin with the /bah/ sound. We use the letters "ba" to write that sound. When we read, the letters "ba" tell us to say /bah/.

Point to the picture whose name begins with the letters "ba."

ba

bat, beet

ba

rag, bag, big

ba

dad, bed, bad

Children who are able to print may find their memory benefits from writing the letters under the correct picture, but asking this of preschool or kindergarten students may prove distracting to the reading lesson.

Activity 20: Consonant With Short Vowel Sound – ba

Point to the picture whose name begins with the letters "ba."

ba         

badge, bridge, bend

ba         

biscuit, bucket, basket

ba      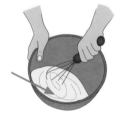   

butter, batter, boxer

ba         

black, battle, bottle

    ©2015 The Critical Thinking Co.™ • www.CriticalThinking.com • 800-458-4849

Activity 20: Consonant With Short Vowel Sound – ba

Point to the picture whose name begins with the letters "ba."

ba

best, bath, Beth

ba

bench, bunch, bandage

ba

bobcat, buckle, backpack

ba

baboon, bubble, bedroom

Activity 21:   Consonant With Short Vowel Sound - be

Words like bed, beg, and bench all begin with the /beh/ sound. We use the letters "be" to write that sound. When we read, the letters "be" tell us to say /beh/.

Point to the picture whose name begins with the letters "be."

be

bent, bite

be

bill, ball, bell

be

bend, den, band

Activity 21: Consonant With Short Vowel Sound – be

Point to the picture whose name begins with the letters "be."

be         

bomb, bath, Beth

be         

belt, buck, back

be         

baby, butter, bedroom

be         

bush, best, bus

Activity 22: Consonant With Short Vowel Sound - bi

Words like big, bill, and bicker all begin with the /bih/ sound. We use the letters "bi" to write that sound. When we read, the letters "bi" tell us to say /bih/.

Point to the picture whose name begins with the letters "bi."

bi

bib, Bob

bi

 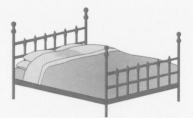 

bud, bed, bid

bi

boot, bit, bat

Activity 22: Consonant With Short Vowel Sound – bi

Point to the picture whose name begins with the letters "bi."

bi

bent, bun, bin

bi

bill, bowl, bull

bi

biscuit, bucket, basket

bi

dinner, bigger, bench

Activity 23: Consonant With Short Vowel Sound - bo

Words like box, bottle, and bobcat all begin with the /boh/ sound. We use the letters "bo" to write that sound. When we read, the letters "bo" tell us to say /boh/.

Point to the picture whose name begins with the letters "bo."

bo

bed, body

bo

bun, bomb, Ben

bo

boxer, buckle, backpack

Activity 23: Consonant With Short Vowel Sound – bo

Point to the picture whose name begins with the letters "bo."

bo

button, bottom, bumper

bo

ball, battle, bottle

bo

bonnet, bunny, bent

bo

blocks, bib, Bob

Activity 24: Consonant With Short Vowel Sound - bu

Words like bud, bunny, and buffalo all begin with the /buh/ sound. We use the letters "bu" to write that sound. When we read, the letters "bu" tell us to say /buh/.

Point to the picture whose name begins with the letters "bu."

bu

bug, bag

bu

back, beak, buck

bu

brush, bus, dust

Activity 24:   Consonant With Short Vowel Sound – bu

Point to the picture whose name begins with the letters "bu."

bu

bent, bun, bin

bu

butter, boater, batter

bu

baby, baboon, bubble

bu

basket, bucket, boxer

Learning to Read: Consonants and Co-Articulation

 This is the letter "c." The letter "c" looks like this:

c   C

"C" makes the beginning sound of castle, cop, and cuff.

castle

cop

cuff

The letters "ce," "ci," and "cy" are used to spell the "s" sound, as in cent, city, and cycle. This is often called a "soft c." (The letter "k" is used to spell words that require the short "e" or short "i" sound, as in kennel and kitten.) Students will study these "soft c" words in Part 2. Therefore, there are only three co-articulation lessons ("ca," "co," "cu") for the letter "c."

Activity 25: Consonant With Short Vowel Sound - ca

Words like cat, cash, and cabin all begin with the /cah/ sound. We use the letters "ca" to write that sound. When we read, the letters "ca" tell us to say /cah/.

Point to the picture whose name begins with the letters "ca."

ca   

cap, cop

ca      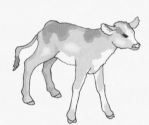   

coffee, calf, cuff

ca         

cob, cab, crab

Activity 25: Consonant With Short Vowel Sound – ca

Point to the picture whose name begins with the letters "ca."

ca

cotton, king, cabin

ca

castle, collar, kid

ca

comet, cabbage, cupboard

ca

cactus, kick, costume

Activity 26: Consonant With Short Vowel Sound - co

Words like cop, cob, and costume all begin with the /coh/ sound. We use the letters "co" to write that sound. When we read, the letters "co" tell us to say /coh/.

Point to the picture whose name begins with the letters "co."

CO

cot, cat

CO

clock, comet, camera

CO

comic, cuff, kick

Activity 26: Consonant With Short Vowel Sound – co

Point to the picture whose name begins with the letters "co."

CO         

cotton, candle, cuddle

CO      

cupcake, copper, cupboard

CO         

castle, concert, customer

CO         

camel, call, collar

Activity 27: Consonant With Short Vowel Sound - cu

Words like cut, cuss, and cupcake all begin with the /cuh/ sound. We use the letters "cu" to write that sound. When we read, the letters "cu" tell us to say /cuh/.

Point to the picture whose name begins with the letters "cu."

cu

cup, cop

cu

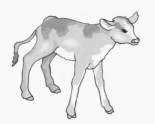  

calf, cuff, coffee

cu

club, cab, cub

Activity 27: Consonant With Short Vowel Sound – cu

Point to the picture whose name begins with the letters "cu."

cu

castle, costume, customer

cu

cotton, cutout, kite

cu

cuddle, kettle, candle

cu

camera, copper, cupboard

Learning to Read: Consonants and Co-Articulation

 This is the letter "d." The letter "d" looks like this:

d   D

"D" makes the beginning sound of dab, deli, dig, dock, and dummy.

dab

deli

dig

dock

dummy

Activity 28: Consonant With Short Vowel Sound - da

Words like dad, dazzle, and daffy all begin with the /dah/ sound. We use the letters "da" to write that sound. When we read, the letters "da" tell us to say /dah/.

Point to the picture whose name begins with the letters "da."

da

dash, dish

da

dad, dead, dome

da

drag, dagger, dog

Activity 28: Consonant With Short Vowel Sound – da

Point to the picture whose name begins with the letters "da."

da

dime, dab, dip

da

dresser, dinner, dancer

da

devil, daffodil, duffel

da

dumbbell, doctor, dashboard

Activity 29: Consonant With Short Vowel Sound - de

Words like dent, desk, and deli all begin with the /deh/ sound. We use the letters "de" to write that sound. When we read, the letters "de" tell us to say /deh/.

Point to the picture whose name begins with the letters "de."

de

duck, deck

de

dead, dress, dip

de

Dan, den, dunk

Activity 29: Consonant With Short Vowel Sound – de

Point to the picture whose name begins with the letters "de."

de

dive, devil, dove

de

domino, dummy, denim

de

desert, dizzy, daisy

de

dancer, dentist, doctor

Activity 30:   Consonant With Short Vowel Sound – di

Words like dig, dim, and dinner all begin with the /dih/ sound. We use the letters "di" to write that sound. When we read, the letters "di" tell us to say /dih/."

Point to the picture whose name begins with the letters "di."

di

dip, drip

di

dash, dodge, dish

di

dancer, dizzy, daisy

Activity 30: Consonant With Short Vowel Sound – di

Point to the picture whose name begins with the letters "di."

di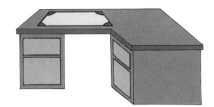

disc, desk, dusk

di

dollar, dinner, dentist

di

deli, doll, dimple

di

desert, disguise, dungeon

Activity 31: Consonant With Short Vowel Sound - do

Words like dot, doll, and documents all begin with the /doh/ sound. We use the letters "do" to write that sound. When we read, the letters "do" tell us to say /doh/.

Point to the picture whose name begins with the letters "do."

do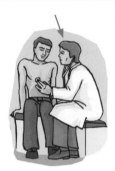

dagger, doctor

do

dollar, deli, dummy

do

dot, dig, drop

Activity 31: Consonant With Short Vowel Sound – do

Point to the picture whose name begins with the letters "do."

do

duck, dock, deck

do

dumbbell, denim, domino

do

digit, dodge, dungeon

do

Debbie, Diane, Donna

Activity 32: Consonant With Short Vowel Sound - du

Words like duck, dunk, and dust all begin with the /duh/ sound. We use the letters "du" to write that sound. When we read, the letters "du" tell us to say /duh/.

Point to the picture whose name begins with the letters "du."

du

desk, dusk

du

 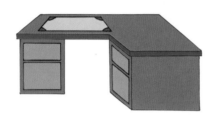 

daisy, dogs, dummy

du

dump, dome, drum

Activity 32: Consonant With Short Vowel Sound – du

Point to the picture whose name begins with the letters "du."

du

dumpster, dentist, dimple

du

digit, dodge, dungeon

du

dumbbell, doll, deli

du

daffodil, duffel, dollar

Learning to Read: Consonants and Co-Articulation

 This is the letter "f." The letter "f" looks like this:

f F

"F" makes the beginning sound of fast, fence, fix, fox, and fun.

fast

fence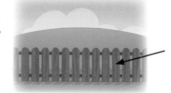

fix

fox

fun

Activity 33: Consonant With Short Vowel Sound - fa

Words like fact, fashion, and fabulous all begin with the /fah/ sound. We use the letters "fa" to write that sound. When we read, the letters "fa" tell us to say /fah/.

Point to the picture whose name begins with the letters "fa."

fa

fist, fast

fa

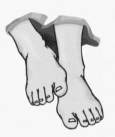  

feet, fit, fat

fa

fix, fashion, phone

Activity 33:   Consonant With Short Vowel Sound – fa

Point to the picture whose name begins with the letters "fa."

fa

flag, fumble, fabric

fa

fiddle, family, funnel

fa

fasten, fossil, festival

fa

factory, fetch, foxhole

Activity 34: Consonant With Short Vowel Sound - fe

Words like fed, fell, and February all begin with the /feh/ sound. We use the letters "fe" to write that sound. When we read, the letters "fe" tell us to say /feh/.

Point to the picture whose name begins with the letters "fe."

fe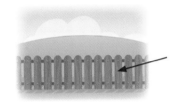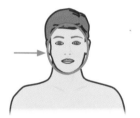

fence, face

fe

fudge, fish, fetch

fe

father, feather, farmer

Activity 34: Consonant With Short Vowel Sound – fe

Point to the picture whose name begins with the letters "fe."

fe

fishing, fencing, factory

fe

fist, fast, festival

fe

fall, felon, fill

fe

fender, finger, fundraiser

Activity 35: Consonant With Short Vowel Sound - fi

Words like *fist*, *fifty*, and *finish* all begin with the /fih/ sound. We use the letters "fi" to write that sound. When we read, the letters "fi" tell us to say /fih/."

Point to the picture whose name begins with the letters "fi."

 fi

fin, fan

 fi

feet, fit, flip

 fi

fuzzy, fix, fox

Activity 35: Consonant With Short Vowel Sound – fi

Point to the picture whose name begins with the letters "fi."

fi

fourth, fifth, foot

fi

full, follow, fill

fi

fishing, fossil, fashion

fi

fiddle, funnel, festival

Activity 35:   Consonant With Short Vowel Sound – fi

Point to the picture whose name begins with the letters "fi."

 fi

fist, fast, feast

 fi

fudge, fetch, fish

Activity 36:   Consonant With Short Vowel Sound - fo

Words like fond, font, and fodder all begin with the /foh/ sound. We use the letters "fo" to write that sound. When we read, the letters "fo" tell us to say /foh/.

Point to the picture whose name begins with the letters "fo."

fo

fix, fox

Activity 36: Consonant With Short Vowel Sound – fo

Point to the picture whose name begins with the letters "fo."

fo

fill, follow, felon

fo

fo

fond, fit, flop

fo

fumble, foxhole, factory

Activity 37: Consonant With Short Vowel Sound - fu

Words like fuss, fudge, and funny all begin with the /fuh/ sound. We use the letters "fu" to write that sound. When we read, the letters "fu" tell us to say /fuh/.

Point to the picture whose name begins with the letters "fu."

fu

phone, fun

fu

  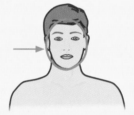

fudge, fetch, face

fu

fuss, fall, follow

Activity 37: Consonant With Short Vowel Sound – fu

Point to the picture whose name begins with the letters "fu."

fu

fuzzy, fossil, fasten

fu

fiddle, family, funnel

fu

fabric, fumble, festival

fu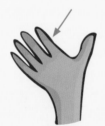

fender, finger, fundraiser

Learning to Read: Consonants and Co-Articulation

 This is the letter "g." The letter "g" looks like this:

g   G

"G" makes the beginning sound of gasoline, gecko, gift, goggles, and gum.

gasoline

gecko

gift

goggles

gum

The letter combinations "ge," "gi" and "gy" are most often used to spell the /j/ sound as in germ, giant, and gym. This is known as a "soft g." Since there are but a few "gi" words (give, gill, giggle) and fewer "ge" words, only three co-articulation lessons ("ga," "go," "gu") for the letter "g" are presented here. Students will study "soft g" words in Part 2.

Activity 38: Consonant With Short Vowel Sound - ga

Words like gab, gadget, and gallon all begin with the /gah/ sound. We use the letters "ga" to write that sound. When we read, the letters "ga" tell us to say /gah/.

Point to the picture whose name begins with the letters "ga."

ga

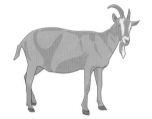

gap, goat, gift

ga

goose, gush, gas

ga

giggle, goggles, gag

Activity 38: Consonant With Short Vowel Sound – ga

Point to the picture whose name begins with the letters "ga."

ga

gum, grab, gab

ga

glasses, gallop, gossip

ga

gavel, guzzle, gobble

ga

gutter, gallery, gondola

Activity 39: Consonant With Short Vowel Sound - go

Words like got, gosh, and gobble all begin with the /goh/ sound. We use the letters "go" to write that sound. When we read, the letters "go" tell us to say /goh/.

Point to the picture whose name begins with the letters "go."

go

geese, gallop, gossip

go

giggle, goggles, gag

go

goblet, guest, gust

Activity 39: Consonant With Short Vowel Sound – go

Point to the picture whose name begins with the letters "go."

go

gavel, gobble, girl

go

guzzle, gosling, glasses

go

goblin, globe, guppy

go

gutter, gallery, gondola

Activity 40: Consonant With Short Vowel Sound - gu

Words like gut, gulp, and gust all begin with the /guh/ sound. We use the letters "gu" to write that sound. When we read, the letters "gu" tell us to say /guh/.

Point to the picture whose name begins with the letters "gu."

gu

game, gum, gab

gu

gas, goose, gush

gu

gut, goat, gift

Activity 40: Consonant With Short Vowel Sound – gu

Point to the picture whose name begins with the letters "gu."

gu

goblin, gap, guppy

gu

gutter, gate, giggle

gu

gull, gallery, glum

gu

gavel, guzzle, gosling

Learning to Read: Consonants and Co-Articulation

 This is the letter "h." The letter "h" looks like this:

h   H

"H" makes the beginning sound of hat, hen, hit, hop, and hug.

hat

hen

hit

hop

hug

Activity 41:   Consonant With Short Vowel Sound - ha

Words like habit, have, and had all begin with the /hah/ sound. We use the letters "ha" to write that sound. When we read, the letters "ha" tell us to say /hah/."

Point to the picture whose name begins with the letters "ha."

ha

hit, hot, hat

ha

hatch, hitch, hut

ha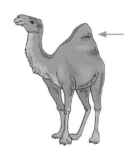

hippo, happy, hump

Activity 41:   Consonant With Short Vowel Sound – ha

Point to the picture whose name begins with the letters "ha."

ha

hive, half, hoof

ha

hatchet, hotdog, hexagon

ha

holly, helmet, hammer

ha

handle, huddle, hidden

Activity 42: Consonant With Short Vowel Sound - he

Words like hem, hello, and headband all begin with the /heh/ sound. We use the letters "he" to write that sound. When we read, the letters "he" tell us to say /heh/.

Point to the picture whose name begins with the letters "he."

he

hen, hand, hunt

he

ham, head, hug

he
  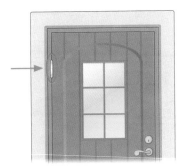

hatch, hedge, hinge

Activity 42: Consonant With Short Vowel Sound – he

Point to the picture whose name begins with the letters "he."

he

hive, hoof, heavy

he

hiker, hockey, hexagon

he

holly, helmet, hammer

he

helicopter, holiday, huckleberry

Activity 43: Consonant With Short Vowel Sound - hi

Words like hiss, him, and hiccup all begin with the /hih/ sound. We use the letters "hi" to write that sound. When we read, the letters "hi" tell us to say /hih/.

Point to the picture whose name begins with the letters "hi."

hi

hit, hat, hut

hi

hop, hip, hoop

hi

hole, hall, hill

Activity 43: Consonant With Short Vowel Sound – hi

Point to the picture whose name begins with the letters "hi."

hi

hatch, hitch, hot

hi

hospital, hippo, happy

hi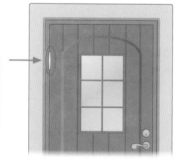

hinge, hedge, hand

hi

handle, huddle, hidden

Activity 44: Consonant With Short Vowel Sound - ho

Words like hop, hobby, and hollow all begin with the /hoh/ sound. We use the letters "ho" to write that sound. When we read, the letters "ho" tell us to say /hoh/.

Point to the picture whose name begins with the letters "ho."

ho

hit, hot, heart

ho

hospital, hexagon, hammer

ho

holly, hilly, helmet

Activity 44: Consonant With Short Vowel Sound – ho

Point to the picture whose name begins with the letters "ho."

ho

hiker, hockey, hippo

ho

handcuffs, hubcap, hopscotch

ho

huckleberry, hamburger, hotdog

ho

helicopter, holiday, hundred

Activity 45: Consonant With Short Vowel Sound - hu

Words like hum, hunch, and husband all begin with the /huh/ sound. We use the letters "hu" to write that sound. When we read, the letters "hu" tell us to say /huh/.

Point to the picture whose name begins with the letters "hu."

hu

hat, hot, hut

hu

hen, hand, hunt

hu

hug, hog, hook

Activity 45:   Consonant With Short Vowel Sound – hu

Point to the picture whose name begins with the letters "hu."

hu

huddle, hidden, hotdog

hu

ham, hump, hoop

hu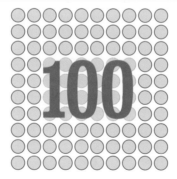

handle, hundred, headband

hu

handcuffs, hopscotch, hubcap

Learning to Read: Consonants and Co-Articulation

 This is the letter "j." The letter "j" looks like this:

j   J

"J" makes the beginning sound of jacket, jet, jiggle, jockey, and juggle.

jacket

jet

jiggle

jockey

juggle

Activity 46: Consonant With Short Vowel Sound - ja

Words like jab, jazz, and Jack all begin with the /jah/ sound. We use the letters "ja" to write that sound. When we read, the letters "ja" tell us to say /jah/.

Point to the picture whose name begins with the letters "ja."

ja

jackal, juggle, jiggle

ja

jogger, jaguar, junkyard

ja

Jesse, jockey, jagged

Activity 46: Consonant With Short Vowel Sound – ja

Point to the picture whose name begins with the letters "ja."

ja   

jacks, Josh, judge

ja   

jump, gym, jam

ja   

jester, janitor, Jennifer

ja   

Jonathan, javelin, jellyfish

Activity 47: Consonant With Short Vowel Sound - je

Words like Jeff, jealous, and jeopardy all begin with the /jeh/ sound. We use the letters "je" to write that sound. When we read, the letters "je" tell us to say /jeh/.

Point to the picture whose name begins with the letters "je."

je

jug, jog, jet

je

Jill, jolly, jelly

je

jester, jumper, Jimmy

Activity 47:   Consonant With Short Vowel Sound – je

Point to the picture whose name begins with the letters "je."

je

Josh, Jesse, juice

je

jockey, jetty, jittery

je

Jennifer, janitor, jungle

je

Jonathan, javelin, jellyfish

Activity 48: Consonant With Short Vowel Sound - ji

Words like jiggle, jiffy, and Jimmy all begin with the /jih/ sound. We use the letters "ji" to write that sound. When we read, the letters "ji" tell us to say /jih/.

Point to the picture whose name begins with the letters "ji."

ji   

jump, jam, Jim

ji         

jug, jig, jet

ji         

Jill, jail, jewel

Activities 48: Consonant With Short Vowel Sound – ji

Point to the picture whose name begins with the letters "ji."

 ji

jester, jittery, jetty

 ji

jackal, juggle, jiggle

Activity 49: Consonant With Short Vowel Sound - jo

 Words like job, jock, and John all begin with the /joh/ sound. We use the letters "jo" to write that sound. When we read, the letters "jo" tell us to say /joh/.

Point to the picture whose name begins with the letters "jo."

 jo

jagged, jug, jog

Activity 49: Consonant With Short Vowel Sound – jo

> ## Point to the picture whose name begins with the letters "jo."

jo

Josh, judge, juice

jo

Jesse, jockey, jacket

jo

jewel, jolly, jelly

jo

jaguar, jogger, junkyard

Activity 50:   Consonant With Short Vowel Sound - ju

Words like justice, junk, and July all begin with the /juh/ sound. We use the letters "ju" to write that sound. When we read, the letters "ju" tell us to say /juh/.

Point to the picture whose name begins with the letters "ju."

ju

jug, jig, jog

ju

jump, gym, jam

ju

jacks, Josh, judge

Activity 50:   Consonant With Short Vowel Sound – ju

Point to the picture whose name begins with the letters "ju."

ju

jackal, juggle, jiggle

ju

Jennifer, janitor, jumper

ju

jagged, jungle, jewel

ju

jogger, jaguar, junkyard

Learning to Read: Consonants and Co-Articulation

This is the letter "k." The letter "k" looks like this:

k   K

"K" makes the beginning sound of kangaroo, kettle, and kitchen.

kangaroo

kettle

kitchen

The sounds associated with "ka," "ko," and "ku" are generally written with a "c" as in cap, cop and cup. Thus there are only two co-articulation lessons on the letter "k."

Activity 51: Consonant With Short Vowel Sound - ke

Words like kelp, kept, and Ken all begin with the /keh/ sound. We use the letters "ke" to write that sound. When we read, the letters "ke" tell us to say /keh/.

Point to the picture whose name begins with the letters "ke."

ke

keg, king, cake

ke

camel, kennel, kitten

ke

cactus, kitchen, ketchup

Activity 51:   Consonant With Short Vowel Sound – ke

Point to the picture whose name begins with the letters "ke."

ke

Kim, can, Ken

ke

cuddle, kettle, candle

ke

cold, call, kelp

ke

coffee, Kevin, cover

Activity 52:   Consonant With Short Vowel Sound - ki

Words like kit, kidney, and kindergarten all begin with the /kih/ sound. We use the letters "ki" to write that sound. When we read, the letters "ki" tell us to say /kih/.

Point to the picture whose name begins with the letters "ki."

ki

comet, kid, cut

ki

cat, coat, kitten

ki

keg, kick, cake

Activity 52: Consonant With Short Vowel Sound – ki

> Point to the picture whose name begins with the letters "ki."

ki

camel, kennel, kibble

ki

kiss, keys, castle

ki

Kim, camera, Ken

ki

kitchen, ketchup, customer

Learning to Read: Consonants and Co-Articulation

This is the letter "l." The letter "l" looks like this:

l   L

"L" makes the beginning sound of ladder, lemon, little, lobster, and lumber.

ladder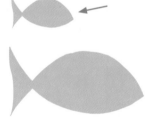

lemon

little

lobster

lumber

Activity 53: Consonant With Short Vowel Sound - la

Words like lab, last, and lack all begin with the /lah/ sound. We use the letters "la" to write that sound. When we read, the letters "la" tell us to say /lah/.

Point to the picture whose name begins with the letters "la."

lip, leap, lap

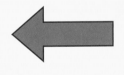

left, lift, laugh

lunch, latch, ledge

Activity 53:   Consonant With Short Vowel Sound – la

Point to the picture whose name begins with the letters "la."

 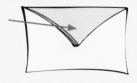

lasso, lizard, limo

flap, lab, lime

last, lettuce, lobster

little, ladder, locker

Activity 54: Consonant With Short Vowel Sound - le

Words like *left*, *leather*, and *lesson* all begin with the /leh/ sound. We use the letters "le" to write that sound. When we read, the letters "le" tell us to say /leh/.

Point to the picture whose name begins with the letters "le."

le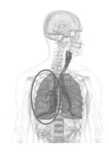

log, lung, leg

le

lemon, limo, lime

le  ABfcdeg

lobster, letters, ladder

Activity 54: Consonant With Short Vowel Sound – le

Point to the picture whose name begins with the letters "le."

le

lunch, ledge, lodge

le

lettuce, licorice, luxury

le

lizard, leopard, lumber

le

luggage, locker, leprechaun

Activity 55: Consonant With Short Vowel Sound - li

 Words like *listen*, *lily*, and *liver* all begin with the /lih/ sound. We use the letters "li" to write that sound. When we read, the letters "li" tell us to say /lih/.

Point to the picture whose name begins with the letters "li"

 li         

lid, lamb, lot

 li      

lock, lake, lick

 li         

little, letter, lumber

Activity 55: Consonant With Short Vowel Sound – li

Point to the picture whose name begins with the letters "li."

lemon, limo, lobby

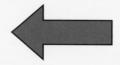

left, lift, laugh

lizard, lasso, lobster

luggage, lettuce, licorice

Activity 56: Consonant With Short Vowel Sound - lo

Words like lob, logic, and lopsided all begin with the /loh/ sound. We use the letters "lo" to write that sound. When we read, the letters "lo" tell us to say /loh/.

Point to the picture whose name begins with the letters "lo."

lo

lock, lake, lick

lo

laptop, lollipop, lullaby

lo

lit, light, lot

Activity 56: Consonant With Short Vowel Sound – lo

Point to the picture whose name begins with the letters "lo."

lo

lunch, ledge, lodge

lo

lasso, lobster, lumber

lo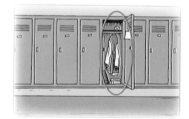

clock, locker, ladder

lo

lemon, limo, lobby

Activity 57: Consonant With Short Vowel Sound - lu

Words like luck, lung, and lush all begin with the /luh/ sound. We use the letters "lu" to write that sound. When we read, the letters "lu" tell us to say /luh/.

Point to the picture whose name begins with the letters "lu."

lu

log, lug, leg

lu

lunch, latch, launch

lu

lamp, lump, leprechaun

Activity 57:   Consonant With Short Vowel Sound – lu

Point to the picture whose name begins with the letters "lu."

lu

lobster, leopard, lumber

lu

laptop, lollipop, lullaby

lu

luggage, lodge, leash

lu

locker, licorice, luxury

Learning to Read: Consonants and Co-Articulation

 This is the letter "m." The letter "m" looks like this:

m   M

"M" makes the beginning sound of map, medal, mitt, model, and mummy.

map

 medal

mitt

model

mummy

Activity 58:   Consonant With Short Vowel Sound - ma

Words like map, mash, and match all begin with the /mah/ sound. We use the letters "ma" to write that sound. When we read, the letters "ma" tell us to say /mah/.

Point to the picture whose name begins with the letters "ma."

ma

mud, mad, mob

ma

mat, mitt, meat

ma

mug, milk, mask

Activity 58: Consonant With Short Vowel Sound – ma

Point to the picture whose name begins with the letters "ma."

ma

magnet, mongoose, monkey

ma

mushroom, meadow, magic

ma

mustache, mascot, missile

ma

megaphone, magazine, medicine

Activity 59: Consonant With Short Vowel Sound - me

Words like mess, melt, and megaphone all begin with the /meh/ sound. We use the letters "me" to write that sound. When we read, the letters "me" tell us to say /meh/.

Point to the picture whose name begins with the letters "me."

me

men, man, moon

me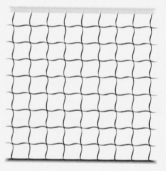

moth, mix, mesh

me

mitten, melon, muffin

Activity 59: Consonant With Short Vowel Sound – me

> Point to the picture whose name begins with the letters "me."

me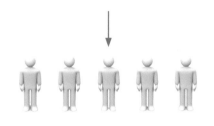

model, middle, medal

me

mixer, measure, monster

me

mushroom, mansion, meadow

me

medicine, mannequin, minivan

Activity 60: Consonant With Short Vowel Sound - mi

Words like mint, mission, and million all begin with the /mih/ sound. We use the letters "mi" to write that sound. When we read, the letters "mi" tell us to say /mih/.

Point to the picture whose name begins with the letters "mi."

mi      

melt, mug, milk

mi         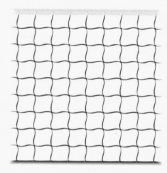

mix, Max, mesh

mi         

mat, mitt, mutt

Activity 60: Consonant With Short Vowel Sound – mi

Point to the picture whose name begins with the letters "mi."

mi

mitten, mantel, muffin

mi

model, middle, medal

mi

missile, muscle, meadow

mi

mustache, mascot, mixer

Activity 61: Consonant With Short Vowel Sound - mo

Words like mom, mock, and modern all begin with the /moh/ sound. We use the letters "mo" to write that sound. When we read, the letters "mo" tell us to say /moh/.

Point to the picture whose name begins with the letters "mo."

mo

map, mop, maid

mo

model, medal, maple

mo

mud, mad, mob

Activity 61:   Consonant With Short Vowel Sound – mo

Point to the picture whose name begins with the letters "mo."

mo

mantel, mug, mock

mo

mixer, monster, mustard

mo

mummy, mongoose, magazine

mo

monitor, mannequin, minivan

Activity 62: Consonant With Short Vowel Sound - mu

 Words like mutt, mumble, and muzzle all begin with the /muh/ sound. We use the letters "mu" to write that sound. When we read, the letters "mu" tell us to say /muh/.

Point to the picture whose name begins with the letters "mu."

mu

mud, mad, maid

mu

mom, mummy, magic

mu

mug, mock, magnet

Activity 62: Consonant With Short Vowel Sound – mu

Point to the picture whose name begins with the letters "mu."

mu

mitten, melon, muffin

mu

missile, muscle, moose

mu

measure, monster, mustard

mu

mushroom, mansion, monitor

Learning to Read: Consonants and Co-Articulation

This is the letter "n." The letter "n" looks like this:

n N

"N" makes the beginning sound of nap, net, nickel, nozzle, and numbers.

nap

net

nickel

nozzle

numbers 1 2 6 7
3 4 5

Activity 63: Consonant With Short Vowel Sound - na

Words like nag, nab, and nasty all begin with the /nah/ sound. We use the letters "na" to write that sound. When we read, the letters "na" tell us to say /nah/.

Point to the picture whose name begins with the letters "na."

na

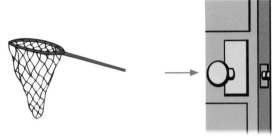

nap, net, knob

na

nun, nag, neck

na

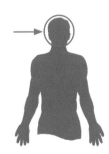

nipple, napkin, noggin

Activity 64:   Consonant With Short Vowel Sound - ne

Words like next, never, and nephew all begin with the /neh/ sound. We use the letters "ne" to write that sound. When we read, the letters "ne" tell us to say /neh/.

Point to the picture whose name begins with the letters "ne."

ne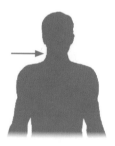

Nick, knock, neck

ne

knit, net, knot

ne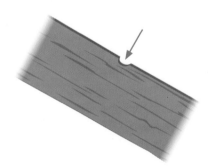

nest, nose, notch

Activity 64: Consonant With Short Vowel Sound – ne

Point to the picture whose name begins with the letters "ne."

nickel, nugget, necklace

nostril, nectar, knight

nozzle, nuzzle, nestling

nectarine, nocturnal, nutcracker

Activity 65:   Consonant With Short Vowel Sound - ni

Words like nip, nifty, and nimble all begin with the /nih/ sound. We use the letters "ni" to write that sound. When we read, the letters "ni" tell us to say /nih/.

Point to the picture whose name begins with the letters "ni."

ni

  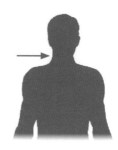

Nick, knock, neck

ni

nickel, nugget, necklace

ni

nutshell, nipple, napkin

Activity 65: Consonant with short vowel sound – ni

Point to the picture whose name begins with the letters "ni."

ni

nun, nanny, ninja

ni

$$12\,6\,7$$
$$3\,4\,5$$

needle, nibble, numbers

Activity 66: Consonant With Short Vowel Sound - no

Words like nod, novel, and nonsense all begin with the /noh/ sound. We use the letters "no" to write that sound. When we read, the letters "no" tell us to say /noh/.

Point to the picture whose name begins with the letters "no."

no

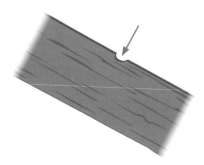

knife, notch, nest

Activity 66:　Consonant With Short Vowel Sound – no

> ### Point to the picture whose name begins with the letters "no."

no

nozzle, nuzzle, needle

no

nostril, nestling, nectar

no

napkin, nugget, noggin

no

nectarine, nocturnal, necklace

Activity 67: Consonant With Short Vowel Sound - nu

Words like nudge, numb, and nutmeg all begin with the /nuh/ sound. We use the letters "nu" to write that sound. When we read, the letters "nu" tell us to say /nuh/.

Point to the picture whose name begins with the letters "nu."

nu

knit, nut, gnat

nu

nun, nanny, nine

nu

nozzle, nuzzle, nipple

Activity 67: Consonant With Short Vowel Sound – nu

Point to the picture whose name begins with the letters "nu."

nu

nickel, nugget, nectarine

nu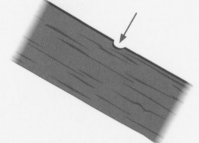

nutshell, notch, nestling

nu  
$$1\ 2\ 6\ 7$$
$$3\ 4\ 5^{7}$$

neighbors, nibble, numbers

nu

nectar, nocturnal, nutcracker

Learning to Read: Consonants and Co-Articulation

 This is the letter "p." The letter "p" looks like this:

p P

"P" makes the beginning sound of package, pencil, pickle, pocket, and pumpkin.

package

pencil

pickle

pocket

pumpkin

Activity 68: Consonant With Short Vowel Sound - pa

Words like pad, pack, and pacifier all begin with the /pah/ sound. We use the letters "pa" to write that sound. When we read, the letters "pa" tell us to say /pah/.

Point to the picture whose name begins with the letters "pa."

pa

pop, peach, path

pa

pedal, puddle, paddle

pa

pillow, palace, plaza

Activity 68: Consonant With Short Vowel Sound – pa

Point to the picture whose name begins with the letters "pa."

pa

package, pocket, picnic

pa

poncho, patch, pitch

pa

pottery, patio, pentagon

pa

passenger, popsicle, pedestal

Activity 69: Consonant With Short Vowel Sound - pe

Words like pebble, peasant, and pest all begin with the /peh/ sound. We use the letters "pe" to write that sound. When we read, the letters "pe" tell us to say /peh/.

Point to the picture whose name begins with the letters "pe."

pe

pan, pin, pen

pe

pedal, paddle, poodle

pe

pickle, petal, puddle

Activity 69: Consonant With Short Vowel Sound – pe

Point to the picture whose name begins with the letters "pe."

pe

penny, pony, panda

pe

paper, pepper, puppet

pe

puzzle, pencil, possum

pe

pigeon, present, pelican

Activity 70: Consonant With Short Vowel Sound - pi

Words like pick, pinch, and picture all begin with the /pih/ sound. We use the letters "pi" to write that sound. When we read, the letters "pi" tell us to say /pih/.

Point to the picture whose name begins with the letters "pi."

 pi

pan, pin, spin

pi

pal, pole, pill

pi

pickle, petal, pocket

Activity 70:   Consonant With Short Vowel Sound – pi

> Point to the picture whose name begins with the letters "pi."

pi

punch, peach, pitch

pi

pillow, palace, pelican

pi

putt, pit, pet

pi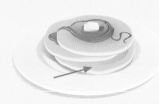

pancake, popcorn, picnic

Activity 71: Consonant With Short Vowel Sound - po

Words like pocket, popular, and pollen all begin with the /poh/ sound. We use the letters "po" to write that sound. When we read, the letters "po" tell us to say /poh/.

Point to the picture whose name begins with the letters "po."

po         (dog)

pop, pipe, pup

po         

pat, pot, pet

po         

pigeon, panda, poncho

Activity 71: Consonant With Short Vowel Sound – po

Point to the picture whose name begins with the letters "po."

po         

pepper, pimple, pompom

po         

passenger, popsicle, pentagon

po         

pottery, patio, pedestal

po         

puzzle, pencil, possum

Activity 72: Consonant With Short Vowel Sound - pu

Words like punish, pump, and puffy all begin with the /puh/ sound. We use the letters "pu" to write that sound. When we read, the letters "pu" tell us to say /puh/.

Point to the picture whose name begins with the letters "pu."

pu

peg, pig, pug

pu

punch, peach, pitch

pu

poodle, puddle, paddle

Activity 72: Consonant With Short Vowel Sound – pu

Point to the picture whose name begins with the letters "pu."

pu

popcorn, pumpkin, penguin

pu

paper, penny, puppy

pu

puzzle, pencil, plum

pu

pepper, pocket, puppet

Learning to Read: Consonant "q" as a Beginning Sound

This is the letter "q." It is always accompanied by the letter "u." The letter "q" looks like this:

q   Q

"Q" makes the beginning sound of quack, question, and quilt.

quack

question

quilt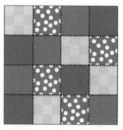

Due to the complexity of spelling and vocabulary, this spelling pattern will be studied in Part 2.

Learning to Read: Consonants and Co-Articulation

This is the letter "r." The letter "r" looks like this:

r   R

"R" makes the beginning sound of rat, register, ribbon, rocket, and rug.

rat

register

ribbon

rocket

rug

Activity 73:   Consonant With Short Vowel Sound - ra

Words like rag, rap, and raccoon all begin with the /rah/ sound. We use the letters "ra" to write that sound. When we read, the letters "ra" tell us to say /rah/.

Point to the picture whose name begins with the letters "ra."

ra

rack, wreck, rock

ra

rush, rich, rash

ra

raft, ref, roof

Activity 73:   Consonant With Short Vowel Sound – ra

> ## Point to the picture whose name begins with the letters "ra."

 ra

ribbon, robin, rabbit

 ra

rattle, ripple, ruffle

ra

rocket, racket, rectangle

ra

rudder, radish, register

Activity 74: Consonant With Short Vowel Sound - re

Words like *ready*, *rebel*, and *restaurant* all begin with the /reh/ sound. We use the letters "re" to write that sound. When we read, the letters "re" tell us to say /reh/."

Point to the picture whose name begins with the letters "re."

re         

rod, road, red

re         

wrist, rest, rose

re         

bread, ref, raft

Activity 74:   Consonant With Short Vowel Sound – re

Point to the picture whose name begins with the letters "re."

re

reptile, ripple, rattle

re

rescue, Rocco, raccoon

re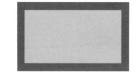

rocket, racket, rectangle

re

runway, raspberry, reservoir

Activity 75: Consonant With Short Vowel Sound - ri

Words like rib, rinse, and rigid all begin with the /rih/ sound. We use the letters "ri" to write that sound. When we read, the letters "ri" tell us to say /rih/."

Point to the picture whose name begins with the letters "ri."

ri

rug, rag, rig

ri

rip, rope, raft

ri

ram, rim, room

Activity 75: Consonant With Short Vowel Sound – ri

> ## Point to the picture whose name begins with the letters "ri."

ri

ribbon, robin, rabbit

ri

wrench, rush, rich

ri

robber, river, ruffle

ri

reptile, ripple, wrapper

Activity 76:   Consonant With Short Vowel Sound - ro

Words like romp, rocky, and rotten all begin with the /roh/ sound. We use the letters "ro" to write that sound. When we read, the letters "ro" tell us to say /roh/."

Point to the picture whose name begins with the letters "ro."

ro

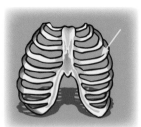      

rib, ref, rob

ro

rod, red, read

ro

rack, wreck, rock

Activity 76: Consonant With Short Vowel Sound – ro

Point to the picture whose name begins with the letters "ro."

ro

ribbon, robin, rabbit

ro

rocket, racket, rung

ro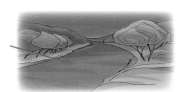

robber, river, rudder

ro

rescue, rocking, raccoon

Activity 77: Consonant With Short Vowel Sound - ru

Words like rub, rust, and rump all begin with the /ruh/ sound. We use the letters "ru" to write that sound. When we read, the letters "ru" tell us to say /ruh/."

Point to the picture whose name begins with the letters "ru."

ru

rug, rag, rig

ru

drum, wren, run

ru

rush, rash, rose

Activity 77: Consonant With Short Vowel Sound – ru

> Point to the picture whose name begins with the letters "ru."

ru

ring, rung, rain

ru

rattle, river, ruffle

ru

radish, rudder, register

ru

runway, radio, trunk

Learning to Read: Consonants and Co-Articulation

 This is the letter "s." The letter "s" looks like this:

s   S

"S" makes the beginning sound of saddle, seven, sister, socket, and sun.

 saddle

seven

sister

socket

sun

Activity 78: Consonant With Short Vowel Sound - sa

Words like sag, sash, and sapphire all begin with the /sah/ sound. We use the letters "sa" to write that sound. When we read, the letters "sa" tell us to say /sah/.

Point to the picture whose name begins with the letters "sa."

sa

sod, seed, sad

sa

sack, sick, sink

sa

soap, sap, soup

Activity 78: Consonant With Short Vowel Sound – sa

Point to the picture whose name begins with the letters "sa."

sa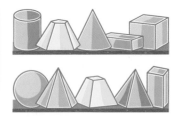

solids, salad, silo

sa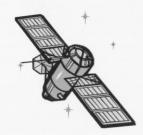

silhouette, satellite, seventeen

sa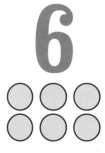

socks, six, saxophone

sa

semicircle, salamander, submarine

Activity 79: Consonant With Short Vowel Sound - se

Words like settle, self, and sesame all begin with the /seh/ sound. We use the letters "se" to write that sound. When we read, the letters "se" tell us to say /seh/."

Point to the picture whose name begins with the letters "se."

se

sit, set, suit

se

sled, sand, send

se

sieve, seven, safe

Activity 79: Consonant With Short Vowel Sound – se

Point to the picture whose name begins with the letters "se."

se      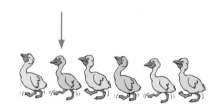   

sickle, second, socket

se         

sucker, soccer, secretary

se         

silhouette, submarine, seventeen

se         

semicircle, salamander, sunflower

Activity 80: Consonant With Short Vowel Sound - si

Words like silk, signal, and sizzle all begin with the /sih/ sound. We use the letters "si" to write that sound. When we read, the letters "si" tell us to say /sih/."

Point to the picture whose name begins with the letters "si."

si

sit, set, seat

si

sip, sap, soup

si

6

sticks, six, sax

Activity 80: Consonant With Short Vowel Sound – si

Point to the picture whose name begins with the letters "si."

si

sickle, second, socket

si

slipper, saddle, sister

si

sandal, sundae, sixteen

si

silver, sapphire, sunflower

Activity 81: Consonant With Short Vowel Sound - so

Words like soggy, sonic, and Solomon all begin with the /soh/ sound. We use the letters "so" to write that sound. When we read, the letters "so" tell us to say /soh/."

Point to the picture whose name begins with the letters "so."

SO

sack, sick, sock

SO

sod, sad, suds

SO

shop, sip, sob

Activity 81: Consonant With Short Vowel Sound – so

Point to the picture whose name begins with the letters "so."

SO

sieve, second, socket

SO

socks, six, sax

SO

sucker, soccer, secretary

SO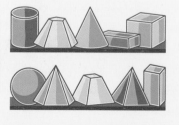

solids, salad, silo

Activity 82: Consonant With Short Vowel Sound - su

Words like sunk, sudden, and summer all begin with the /suh/ sound. We use the letters "su" to write that sound. When we read, the letters "su" tell us to say /suh/."

Point to the picture whose name begins with the letters "su."

su

send, sun, sign

su

sand, seeds, suds

su

supper, saddle, sister

Activity 82: Consonant With Short Vowel Sound – su

Point to the picture whose name begins with the letters "su."

su

sucker, soccer, skunk

su

sandal, sundae, silver

su

salamander, submarine, stump

su

semicircle, sapphire, sunflower

Learning to Read: Consonants and Co-Articulation

 This is the letter "t." The letter "t" looks like this:

 T

"T" makes the beginning sound of tattoo, tent, ticket, top, and tugboat.

tattoo

tent

ticket

top

tugboat

Activity 83: Consonant With Short Vowel Sound - ta

Words like tad, tattle, and talent all begin with the /tah/ sound. We use the letters "ta" to write that sound. When we read, the letters "ta" tell us to say /tah/."

Point to the picture whose name begins with the letters "ta."

ta

tip, top, tap

ta

tug, tag, tiger

ta

  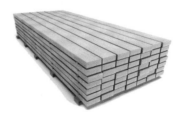

tack, tusk, stack

Activity 83: Consonant With Short Vowel Sound – ta

Point to the picture whose name begins with the letters "ta."

toxic, taxi, tuxedo

tickle, tackle, toddler

tadpole, tiptoe, toadstool

tightrope, telescope, tapestry

Activity 84: Consonant With Short Vowel Sound – te

Words like test, text, and tender all begin with the /teh/ sound. We use the letters "te" to write that sound. When we read, the letters "te" tell us to say /teh/."

Point to the picture whose name begins with the letters "te."

te

tan, tin, ten

te

tied, Ted, toad

te

tent, tongue, tank

Activity 84:   Consonant With Short Vowel Sound – te

Point to the picture whose name begins with the letters "te."

te

tennis, tonsils, tissues

te

topping, temple, tunnel

te

tightrope, telescope, tapestry

te

toadstool, tomahawk, tentacle

Activity 85: Consonant With Short Vowel Sound - ti

Words like tick, tilt, and timid all begin with the /tih/ sound. We use the letters "ti" to write that sound. When we read, the letters "ti" tell us to say /tih/."

Point to the picture whose name begins with the letters "ti."

ti

tan, tin, ten

ti

tip, trip, type

ti

trick, toxic, ticket

Activity 85: Consonant With Short Vowel Sound – ti

> ## Point to the picture whose name begins with the letters "ti."

ti

tummy, timber, tambourine

ti

twins, tickle, toddler

ti

topping, tiptoe, tadpole

ti

teacher, treasure, tissue

Activity 86: Consonant With Short Vowel Sound - to

Words like *tot*, *topple*, and *tonic* all begin with the /toh/ sound. We use the letters "to" to write that sound. When we read, the letters "to" tell us to say /toh/."

Point to the picture whose name begins with the letters "to."

to

tub, top, tap

to

time, team, Tom

to

toxic, taxi, tuxedo

Activity 86:   Consonant With Short Vowel Sound – to

Point to the picture whose name begins with the letters "to."

to

tip, tackle, toddler

to

 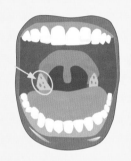 

tennis, tonsil, tunnel

to

topping, temple, tummy

to

telescope, tomahawk, tentacle

Activity 87:   Consonant With Short Vowel Sound - tu

Words like tuck, tussle, and tumble all begin with the /tuh/ sound. We use the letters "tu" to write that sound. When we read, the letters "tu" tell us to say /tuh/."

Point to the picture whose name begins with the letters "tu."

tu

tub, top, tape

tu

tug, tag, tiger

tu

truck, tusk, talk

Activity 87:   Consonant With Short Vowel Sound – tu

Point to the picture whose name begins with the letters "tu."

tu

Tom, tummy, timber

tu
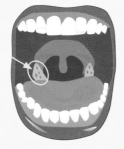  

tonsil, trunk, tunnel

tu

toxic, taxi, tuxedo

tu

tugboat, tiptoe, teacher

Learning to Read: Consonants and Co-Articulation

 This is the letter "v." The letter "v" looks like this:

v   V

"V" makes the beginning sound of valley, vest, video, volleyball, and vulture.

valley

vest

video

volleyball

vulture

Activity 88:   Consonant With Short Vowel Sound - va

"Words like vast, valid, and vaccinate all begin with the /vah/ sound. We use the letters 'va' to write that sound. When we read, the letters 'va' tell us to say /vah/."

Point to the picture whose name begins with the letters "va."

va

vat, vet, vote

va

volume, villain, valley

va

victim, vacuum, Viking

Activity 88: Consonant With Short Vowel Sound – va

Point to the picture whose name begins with the letters "va."

va

veil, valve, violin

va

volcano, video, vanity

va

volleyball, valuables, vegetables

va

vampire, visitor, volunteer

Activity 89: Consonant With Short Vowel Sound - ve

Words like vex, vendor, and veteran all begin with the /veh/ sound. We use the letters "ve" to write that sound. When we read, the letters "ve" tell us to say /veh/."

Point to the picture whose name begins with the letters "ve."

ve
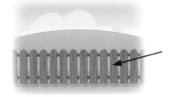

fence, vent, van

ve

vase, vise, vest

ve

venom, vine, victim

Activity 89: Consonant With Short Vowel Sound – ve

Point to the picture whose name begins with the letters "ve."

ve

Velcro®, valve, volcano

ve

volleyball, vigil, vegetables

Activity 90: Consonant With Short Vowel Sound - vi

 Words like vision, village, and victory all begin with the /vih/ sound. We use the letters "vi" to write that sound. When we read, the letters "vi" tell us to say /vih/."

Point to the picture whose name begins with the letters "vi."

vi

Velcro®, vanity, video

Activity 90: Consonant With Short Vowel Sound – vi

Point to the picture whose name begins with the letters "vi."

vi

victim, vacuum, venom

vi

vigil, vulture, vegetables

vi

volume, villain, valley

vi

vampire, visitor, vest

Activity 91: Consonant With Short Vowel Sound - vo

 Words like volley, vomit, and volume all begin with the /voh/ sound. We use the letters "vo" to write that sound. When we read, the letters "vo" tell us to say /voh/."

Point to the picture whose name begins with the letters "vo."

VO

wok, fox, volley

VO

venom, volume, villain

VO

volleyball, valuables, vegetables

VO

visitor, vulture, volunteer

Learning to Read: Consonants and Co-Articulation

This is the letter "w." The letter "w" looks like this:

w

W

"W" makes the beginning sound of wag, web, wind, and wok.

wag

web

wind

wok

There are insufficient "wo" and "wu" words to constitute a lesson.

Activity 92: Consonant With Short Vowel Sound – wa

Words like *wacky* and *waxed* begin with the /wah/ sound. We use the letters "wa" to write that sound. When we read, the letters "wa" tell us to say /wah/."

Point to the picture whose name begins with the letters "wa."

wa

rag, wag, wok

wa

wax, wick, west

wa

weapon, woman, wagon

Activity 93: Consonant With Short Vowel Sound - we

"Words like weather, went, and Wednesday all begin with the /weh/ sound. We use the letters "we" to write that sound. When we read, the letters "we" tell us to say /weh/."

Point to the picture whose name begins with the letters "we."

we  1

web, one, red

we

white, sweat, wet

we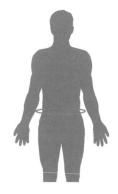

wax, west, waist

Activity 93: Consonant With Short Vowel Sound – we

Point to the picture whose name begins with the letters "we."

we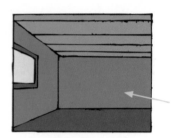

wheel, well, wall

we

wedding, woman, window

we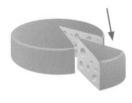

sweater, witch, wedge

we

weapon, wagon, wishbone

Activity 94: Consonant With Short Vowel Sound - wi

Words like winter, willow, and wiggle all begin with the /wih/ sound. We use the letters "wi" to write that sound. When we read, the letters "wi" tell us to say /wih/."

Point to the picture whose name begins with the letters "wi."

wi

wig, wag, rig

wi

web, one, win

wi

watch, witch, rich

Activity 94: Consonant With Short Vowel Sound – wi

Point to the picture whose name begins with the letters "wi."

wi

walk, wick, wok

wi

wind, wand, wood

wi

wedding, wagon, window

wi

weapon, woman, wishbone

Learning to Read: Consonant "x" as an Ending Sound

 This is the letter "x." The letter "x" looks like this:

x   X

"X" makes the ending sound of ax, Rex, mix, ox, and tux."

ax

Rex

mix

ox

tux

Learning to Read: Consonants and Co-Articulation

 This is the letter "y." The letter "y" looks like this:

 y   Y

"Y" makes the beginning sound of yak, yellow, yippee, yonder, and yuck.

yak

yellow

yippee

yonder

yuck

Learning to Read: Consonants and Co-Articulation

This is the letter "z." The letter "z" looks like this:

z   Z

"Z" makes the beginning sound of Zack, zest, zipper, and zombie."

Zack

zest

zipper

zombie

Activity 95: Identifying Beginning Letter Pairs

Point to the letters that begin the word for each picture.

   ba   be   bu

   bo   bi   bu

   ca   co   ce

   ci   co   cu

bench, button, castle, concert

Activity 95: Identifying Beginning Letter Pairs

Point to the letters that begin the word for each picture.

bi   de   di

bu   do   du

fa   fo   fu

fe   fi   fo

disguise, duck, fast, fishing

Activity 95: Identifying Beginning Letter Pairs

Point to the letters that begin the word for each picture.

   ga   ge   gi

   qo   ge   go

   ha   he   hi

   he   hi   ho

gap, goblin, heavy, hippo

Activity 95:   Identifying Beginning Letter Pairs

Point to the letters that begin the word for each picture.

je   jo   go

ja   ge   je

ka   ke   ki

ke   ki   ko

jogger,   jelly,   kitchen,   ketchup

Activity 95:   Identifying Beginning Letter Pairs

Point to the letters that begin the word for each picture.

la   li   lo

le   lo   lu

we   me   mi

mi   me   mo

lock,   lunch,   medal,   mitten

Activity 95: Identifying Beginning Letter Pairs

Point to the letters that begin the word for each picture.

na   no   nu

mu   no   nu

pe   pi   pu

pa   po   pi

---

nozzle,   nut,   pencil,   pitch

Activity 95: Identifying Beginning Letter Pairs

> ### Point to the letters that begin the word for each picture.

ra   ro   re

re   ri   ra

su   si   se

si   so   sa

---

rest, ribbon, seven, sit

Activity 95: Identifying Beginning Letter Pairs

Point to the letters that begin the word for each picture.

to   ta   ti

te   tu   to

va   vi   ve

vi   ve   va

tap,   topping,   vest,   villain

Activity 95:   Identifying Beginning Letter Pairs

> Point to the letters that begin the word for each picture.

wa   we   wo

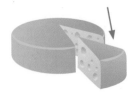

wo   wu   wi

yi   ye   ya

zo   ze   zi

---

wedge,   window,   yellow,   zipper

Activity 96: Co-Articulating Initial Sounds

Say the sounds of the two letters together, then point to the picture whose name starts with those letters.

ba

bi

co

cu

basket, bucket, bush   *bottle, big, bedroom*   *cuff, cop, candle*   *cob, cab, cub*

Activity 96: Co-Articulating Inital Sounds

de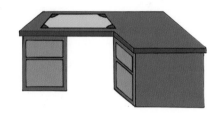

do

fa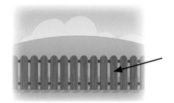

fi

bend, dinner, desk   *duck, doctor, boxer*   *fence, fox, fat*   *fin, fan, fun*

Activity 96: Co-Articulating Inital Sounds

> Say the sounds of the two letters together, then point to the picture whose name starts with those letters.

gu

ga

he

hi

---

goose, gush, gas   *golf, gag, gift*   *hen, hand, hunt*   *handle, huddle, hidden*

Activity 96: Co-Articulating Inital Sounds

> Say the sounds of the two letters together, then point to the picture whose name starts with those letters.

jo

ju

ki

ke

---

jagged, jug, jog   *jockey, juggle, jacket*   *kick, ketchup, kangaroo*   *cuddle, kettle, kitten*

Activity 96: Co-Articulating Inital Sounds

Say the sounds of the two letters together, then point to the picture whose name starts with those letters.

le

li

mo

me

laptop, lollipop, lettuce   *little, letters, ladder*   *model, middle, medal*   *medicine, mannequin, minivan*

Activity 96: Co-Articulating Inital Sounds

Say the sounds of the two letters together, then point to the picture whose name starts with those letters.

nu      ...

ni

pa      ...

pe

needle, nibble, numbers   *nickel, nutcracker, nest*   *pedal, paddle, poodle*   *punch, penny, pitch*

Activity 96:   Co-Articulating Inital Sounds

Say the sounds of the two letters together, then point to the picture whose name starts with those letters.

ro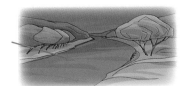

ri

se

su

robber, river, ruffle   *wrench, rush, rich*   *sick, second, socket*   *sucker, soccer, secretary*

Activity 96: Co-Articulating Inital Sounds

> Say the sounds of the two letters together, then point to the picture whose name starts with those letters.

te

ti

ve

va

tennis, tonsils, tissues   *taxi, tusk, ticket*   *volleyball, vulture, vegetables*   *volume, villain, valley*

Activity 96: Co-Articulating Inital Sounds

Say the sounds of the two letters together, then point to the picture whose name starts with those letters.

we

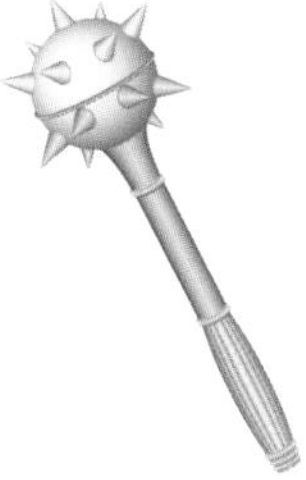

wi

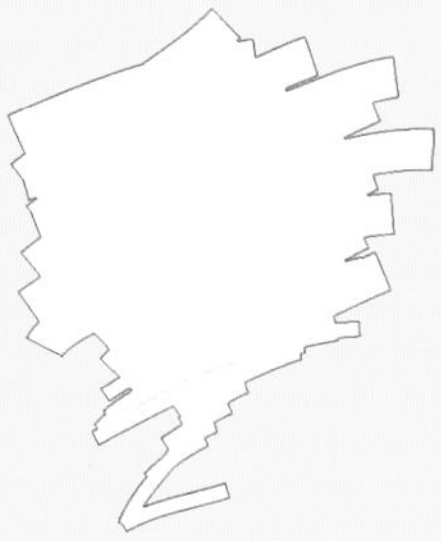

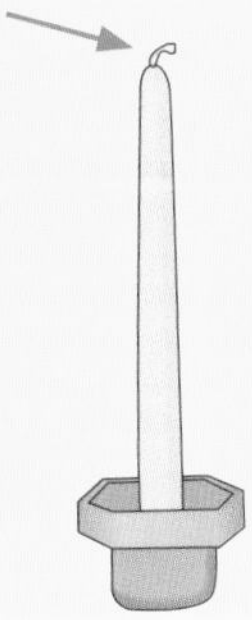

yu

zi

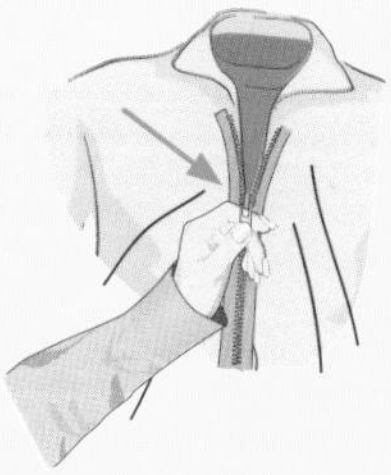

weapon, wagon, wok   *white, wick, west*   *yolk, yuck, yak*   *zoo, zebra, zipper*

Activity 97: Identifying Ending Letters

Point to the letter that ends the word for each picture.

ca_   p   t   c

be_   d   b   z

li_   p   d   b

ho_   k   g   j

---

cat, bed, lip, hog

Activity 97: Identifying Ending Letters

> Point to the letter that ends the word for each picture.

 gu_   m   n   w

 pi_   m   u   n

 bu_   r   s   t

 da_   d   b   p

gum, pin, bus, dab

Activity 97: Identifying Ending Letters

Point to the letter that ends the word for each picture.

a_   t   k   x

u_   p   b   d

i_   m   n   w

o_   k   x   s

ax, up, in, ox

Activity 97:   Identifying Ending Letters

Point to the letter that ends the word for each picture.

we_   w   d   t

ma_   b   d   m

co_   p   t   b

di_   p   g   d

wet,   mad,   cop,   dig

Activity 97: Identifying Ending Letters

> ## Point to the letter that ends the word for each picture.

ru_   n   m   r

bi_   b   d   p

pi_   g   ll   t

cu_   t   b   ff

run, bib, pill, cuff

Activity 98: Identifying Middle Letters

"The middle sound in a word is called the vowel."

Point to the letter for the vowel sound in each picture.

g_m   a   i   u

p_n   i   o   u

c_p   e   o   u

m_n   e   o   u

gum, pin, cop   men

Activity 98: Identifying Middle Letters

Point to the letter for the vowel sound in each picture.

   h_t   a   e   i

   j_t   e   i   o

   m_d   a   o   u

   r_b   e   o   u

hat, jet, mud, rob

Activity 98: Identifying Middle Letters

Point to the letter for the vowel sound in each picture.

w_n   e   i   u

t_g   a   o   u

c_t   a   o   u

w_x   a   o   u

win, tag, cut, wax

Activity 98: Identifying Middle Letters

Point to the letter for the vowel sound in each picture.

l_p   e   i   u

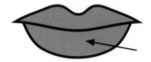

t_p   o   i   u

h_n   e   i   o

f_x   a   i   o

lip, top, hen, fix

Activity 98: Identifying Middle Letters

> Point to the letter for the vowel sound in each picture.

   l_g   a   e   i

   c_b   a   o   u

   s_n   i   o   u

h_ll   a   i   u

leg, cab, sun, hill

Activity 99:   Reading First Words

When reading these words, be sure to look at the middle letter first. Then say the beginning and middle sounds together, before adding the ending sound. Try saying the word out loud once again.

Read the word and point to the correct picture.

bed

cat

dig

fun

---

bud, bed, bad   cap, cut, cat   big, dig, dog   fin, fan, fun

Activity 99: Reading First Words

Read the word and point to the correct picture.

gas         

hop         

jog         

kid         

goose, geese, gas   *hip, hop, happy*   *jug, jig, jog*   *kite, kid, cot*

Activity 99:   Reading First Words

Read the word and point to the correct picture.

leg

mop

nut

pig

---

log, ledge, leg   *map, mop, mob*   *nut, net, knot*   *big, dig, pig*

Activity 99: Reading First Words

Read the word and point to the correct picture.

red

sip

ten

tip

road, red, rip   *zip, sap, sip*   *tan, tin, ten*   *tip, type, tap*

Activity 99: Reading First Words

Read the word and point to the correct picture.

vat

wet

yak

zip

vat, vet, vote   *white, wet, water*   *yolk, yuck, yak*   *sip, zoo, zip*

Activity 99: Reading First Words

Read the word and point to the correct picture.

cup

den

fox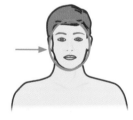

gum

cup, cap, cub   *Dan, den, denim*   *fix, fox, face*   *gut, gym gum*

Activity 99: Reading First Words

Read the word and point to the correct picture.

hat

jet

lip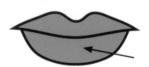

mud

hit, hot, hat   *jelly, jet, jester*   *lip, lick, lap*   *mustard, mud, mad*

Activity 99: Reading First Words

Read the word and point to the correct picture.

nap      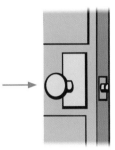

pot         

run      

six      

gnat, nap, knob   *pit, pet, pot*   *run, ring, nun*   *socks, six, sax*

Activity 100: Reading for Meaning

> Read the words and point to the correct picture.

sad kid

red cap

wet cat

mad mom

Activity 100:   Reading for Meaning

Read the words and point to the correct picture.

six men

hot pot

box top

cut leg

Activity 100: Reading for Meaning

> Read the words and point to the correct picture.

bad dog

big bell

fat bug

red gum

Activity 100: Reading for Meaning

> Read the words and point to the correct picture.

tin cup

in bed

ten eggs

Dad runs.

Problem 4 on this page is a complete sentence. Draw student attention to the capital used to start a sentence and the period, which is silent but signals the end of the thought.

Activity 100: Reading For Meaning

Read the words and point to the correct picture.

not fun

not lit

not wet

not hot

Words I Can Read

at	cap	had	mad	pad	sat
ax	cat	hat	map	pat	tag
bad	fat	jab	mat	rag	tap
bag	fax	lab	Max	rap	tax
bat	gag	lad	nag	rat	wag
cab	gap	lap	nap	sad	wax

bed	egg	led	peg	ten	bell
beg	fed	leg	pen	web	fell
Ben	hen	let	pet	wed	sell
bet	Jen	men	red	wet	tell
den	jet	met	set	yes	well
Ed	keg	net	Ted	yet	yell

bib	fin	Jim	pin	sit	bill
bid	fit	kid	pit	six	Bill
big	fix	kit	rib	Tim	fill
bin	hid	lid	rid	tin	hill
bit	him	lip	rig	tip	ill
did	hip	lit	rim	wig	Jill
dig	hit	mix	rip	win	pill
dim	in	nip	sin	wit	will
dip	it	pig	sip	zip	

Words I Can Read

bob	cot	hot	mom	pop	Tom
Bob	dog	job	mop	pot	top
box	dot	jog	nod	rob	tot
cob	fox	log	not	rod	doll
cod	hog	lot	on	rot	
cop	hop	mob	ox	sod	

bud	cup	hug	mug	run	yum
bug	cut	hum	nun	sun	cuff
bun	fun	hut	nut	tub	huff
bus	gum	jug	pup	tug	puff
but	gun	lug	rub	up	
cub	Gus	mud	rug	us	